LIFE SCIENCE LIBRARY

THE BODY

OTHER BOOKS
BY THE
EDITORS OF LIFE

LIFE WORLD LIBRARY

LIFE NATURE LIBRARY

THE LIFE HISTORY OF THE UNITED STATES

LIFE PICTORIAL ATLAS OF THE WORLD

THE EPIC OF MAN

THE WONDERS OF LIFE ON EARTH

THE WORLD WE LIVE IN

THE WORLD'S GREAT RELIGIONS

THE LIFE BOOK OF CHRISTMAS

LIFE'S PICTURE HISTORY OF WESTERN MAN

THE LIFE TREASURY OF AMERICAN FOLKLORE

AMERICA'S ARTS AND SKILLS

THE SECOND WORLD WAR

LIFE'S PICTURE HISTORY OF WORLD WAR II

PICTURE COOK BOOK

LIFE GUIDE TO PARIS

LIFE SCIENCE LIBRARY

CONSULTING EDITORS
René Dubos
Henry Margenau
C. P. Snow

THE BODY

by Alan E. Nourse
and the Editors of LIFE

TIME INCORPORATED, NEW YORK

A STONEHENGE BOOK

ABOUT THIS BOOK

THERE ARE MANY POSSIBLE APPROACHES to a study of the human body, but the most basic is to begin with an examination of how the body is constructed and how it functions. These two fundamentals form the theme of this book. The major organ systems of the body are explained in the light of the most recent discoveries of medical research.

The book contains both text chapters and picture essays. Each essay complements the chapter it follows, illustrating the subject in depth or adding to the information already supplied. Together, chapters and essays make up a unified whole, but each is self-contained and can be read independently. As an example: Chapter 3, "The Team of Bone and Muscle," is followed by an essay in which structural shapes found in engineering and architecture are matched with almost identical functional forms in the human skeleton.

THE AUTHOR

ALAN E. NOURSE, a practicing physician in North Bend, Washington, launched his writing career in order to help pay his way through the University of Pennsylvania Medical School, where he received his M.D. degree in 1951. Co-author of *Management of a Medical Practice*, he has also written *So You Want to Be a Doctor*, a guide for students contemplating a future in medicine. Another book by Dr. Nourse is *Nine Planets*, on the solar system, published in 1960.

THE CONSULTING EDITORS

RENE DUBOS, member and professor of The Rockefeller Institute, is a microbiologist and experimental pathologist world-famous for his pioneering in antibiotics, including the discovery of tyrothricin. He has written, among other books, *Mirage of Health* and *The Dreams of Reason*.

HENRY MARGENAU is Eugene Higgins professor of physics and natural philosophy at Yale, an editor of the *American Journal of Science* and a notable contributor to spectroscopy and nuclear physics. His books include *Open Vistas* and *The Nature of Physical Reality*.

C.P. SNOW has won an international audience for his novels, including *The New Men, The Search* and *The Affair*, which explore the scientist's role in contemporary society. Trained as a physicist, he directed recruitment of scientific personnel for Britain's Ministry of Labour in World War II. He was knighted in 1957.

ON THE COVER

The pliant strength of the human torso, evoked in a bronze by Auguste Rodin, is a quality of the body investigated throughout history by artist and scientist alike. On the back cover is a rendering of an analytic drawing by Leonardo da Vinci of the body's proportions.

CONTENTS

TIME-LIFE BOOKS

EDITOR
Norman P. Ross
TEXT DIRECTOR   ART DIRECTOR
William Jay Gold   Edward A. Hamilton
CHIEF OF RESEARCH
Beatrice T. Dobie
Assistant to the Editor: Carl Solberg
Assistant Text Director: Jerry Korn
Assistant Chief of Research: Monica O. Horne

PUBLISHER
Rhett Austell
General Manager: John A. Watters
Business Manager: John D. McSweeney
Circulation Manager: Joan D. Lanning

LIFE MAGAZINE

EDITOR: Edward K. Thompson
MANAGING EDITOR: George P. Hunt
PUBLISHER: Jerome S. Hardy

LIFE SCIENCE LIBRARY

Editorial staff for *The Body:*
DEPUTY EDITOR: Robert G. Mason
Text Editor: Diana Hirsh
Assistant to the Editor: Simone Daro Gossner
Designer: Arnold C. Holeywell
Associate Designer: Edwin Taylor
Staff Writers: Timothy Carr, Stephen Espie,
Harvey B. Loomis, Peter Meyerson, Paul Trachtman
Chief Researcher: Sheila Osmundsen
Researchers: David Beckwith, Sarah Bennett,
Valentin Y. L. Chu, Doris C. Coffin,
Mary Elizabeth Davidson, Leah Dunaief,
Elizabeth Evans, Emily Heine, Donald Hinkle,
Mary-Jo Kline, Robert R. McLaughlin,
Victor H. Waldrop
Picture Researchers: Margaret K. Goldsmith,
Joan Lynch
Art Associate: Robert L. Young
Art Assistants: James D. Smith,
Charles Mikolaycak, Douglas B. Graham
Copy Staff: Marian Gordon Goldman,
Suzanne Seixas, Dolores A. Littles

The text for the chapters of this book was written by Alan E. Nourse, for the picture essays by the editorial staff. The following individuals and departments of Time Inc. were helpful in producing the book: Alfred Eisenstaedt, Eliot Elisofon, Fritz Goro, Robert W. Kelley, Nina Leen and George Silk, LIFE staff photographers; Bernard P. Spring, Technology Editor, ARCHITECTURAL FORUM; Margaret Sargent, LIFE film editor; Doris O'Neil, Chief, LIFE Picture Library; Richard M. Clurman, Chief, TIME-LIFE News Service; and Content Peckham, Chief, Bureau of Editorial Reference.

INTRODUCTION

MOST OF US—particularly artists and people in love—have some esthetic appreciation of the body's outward form. Few of us take the time to understand its inner structure and functions—which are far more complex than any computer or mechanical invention, yet simple and economical in principle. Form and function meld to produce a body of great efficiency and almost incredible flexibility. With a body less efficient and less flexible, man could not withstand the strains of living in a world where he is constantly forced to adapt himself to everything from pesticides, drugs, tobacco and automobiles to the weightless, oxygenless, foodless world of outer space.

Man can understand, at least in part, how he is made. It is clear that the pattern of the body is set in the beginning. This is his genetic heritage, whereby his future characteristics are transmitted by particular kinds of protein molecules. In a sense, his body is predetermined, but time and environment will determine what happens to it.

When, if ever, man will understand *why* he is made is something else. And whether he will ever understand the relationship between that most complex part of his physical equipment, the brain, and the imponderable and immeasurable thought processes associated with it, is another moot question.

But the body, at least, is comprehensible to science. Unfortunately, scientists do not always make themselves comprehensible to the lay public. This book does. No layman can read it without an increased understanding of the body. Understanding the body leads to increased admiration and respect for it, and such admiration and respect leads, for most of us I suspect, to greater awe of its Maker.

—IRVINE H. PAGE, M.D.
Director, Research Division
The Cleveland Clinic

1

A Uniquely Adaptable Organism

"IN MY VIEW," wrote Thomas Jefferson in 1814, "no knowledge can be more satisfactory to a man than that of his own frame, its parts, their functions and actions." Distinguished thinkers before and since Jefferson have held this belief, but, curiously, it is not one which the average person wholeheartedly shares. Man's attitude toward his own body— his single most precious possession—is decidedly ambivalent. At one and the same time he is fascinated by it and fearful of it, partly in echo of ancient taboos, partly in the conviction that the body is too complicated to understand.

Rarely does man resolve this contradiction. What makes his body tick is both a subject of avid interest—sometimes too avid, as any doctor with hypochondriac patients can testify—and a matter of deliberate unconcern. Except in time of illness, the body itself encourages any tendency to ignore it. Normally, it demands little of its owner but food, clothing and shelter. Such vital functions as breathing and digestion proceed whether we heed them or not. Even when something breaks down, the body tries to repair the damage automatically and unnoticed.

The possible approaches to a study of the body are legion. To the cynic, the body is no more than a tenement of clay; to the poet, a palace of the soul; to the physician, an all-too-ailing hulk. The psychiatrist sees it as a housing for the mind and personality. The geneticist sees it as a perpetuator of its own kind. The biologist sees it as an organism which can alter the future as a result of the experience of the past. The anthropologist sees it as an accumulator of culture. Others have viewed the body as essentially just a machine, a concept that sometimes appeals and sometimes appalls. The English satirist, Samuel Butler, dismissed his fellow man as but "a pair of pincers set over a bellows and a stewpan and the whole thing fixed upon stilts." To the more reverent, the bodily mechanism is a masterpiece of precise planning, a delicate and complex apparatus whose various components work as a unit to achieve such diverse feats as scaling a mountaintop, building a bridge or composing a symphony.

All the specialized scientific views of the body are valid. All, however, must start from the same premise: an awareness of the body's basic structure and functions—its anatomy and physiology. This approach— the one which we shall take in these pages—is the broadest avenue to understanding. Used by investigators throughout history, it has led to most of what we know of the body today.

In this area of human knowledge, as in so many others, the 20th Century, with its remarkable new tools and techniques, has immeasurably added to our comprehension. Instruments have been devised to allow a direct look into the stomach's interior, or to excise a bit of bladder tissue for testing, or to extract fragments of liver or bone marrow for scrutiny.

THE HUMAN COMPLEX
From the beginning, the human body has provided a never-failing source of wonderment to its owner, to the artist celebrating its beauties, to the medical scientist probing its intricately meshed systems. As in other basic areas of knowledge, increased understanding of the body's structure and functions has led to an increased respect for its immense complexity.

Radioactive tracers, ingested into the body, help clarify complicated chemical reactions even as they occur. X-ray diagnosis has been elevated to a high art. What had been invisible under the finest microscope is now detectable by electron bombardment—electron microscopy, so called.

Through these and myriad other devices, vital information about the body, hitherto unprovable, has been established: the fact that the body is made up of an estimated 60 trillion cells; that these cells join together to form basic types of tissue; that these tissues, in turn, are pieced together into complex organ systems; that the body thinks, moves, observes the world around it, enjoys pleasure and suffers pain only as a result of chemical reactions.

The triumph of a bridge

The sum total of what we know about the body to date represents a confluence of the work of doctor and scientist, of clinician as well as of researcher. Laboratory findings in physics, chemistry, physiology, microbiology, immunology and many other fields are ever more crucial to the physician. The results he obtains therefrom, in treating his patients, are essential to further research. So constant is the interchange that medicine, more effectively than any other discipline, has bridged the gap between art and science—the art of individual healing and the science of impersonal knowledge. The fusion was a long time coming. It has become incontrovertible fact only in our own day—a slow but inevitable result of the rise of the scientific method some 300 years ago.

Centuries before then, however, there were the precursors of today's doctors and scientists—the healers and the experimentalists. But the men who were more interested in making empirical deductions about the body per se were (and still are) far outnumbered by those more interested in tending to a particular person's health. Thus man's first knowledge of the body was largely compiled from specific case histories. Dealing with the body in disrepair, physicians of old drew innumerable conclusions about the body in health. Their judgments were often shallow or entirely in error, yet sometimes astonishingly accurate.

The Chinese promulgated all manner of rules for healthful living, such as regular exercise, avoidance of improperly cooked foods, and the use of mouthwash; no less a sage than Confucius himself cautioned, "Diseases enter by the mouth." The Hebrews—as any reader of the Old Testament will recall—laid down a doctrine of sanitation in food, water and bodily care that has persisted to this day. Probably the most knowing about the body among ancient peoples were the Egyptians. The Edwin Smith Papyrus, named for its 19th Century American discoverer and dated 1700 B.C., not only is the oldest surgical treatise extant but also reveals that the Egyptians recognized a relationship between the heart and

A GOD'S EYE AND A DOCTOR'S PRESCRIPTION

THE EYE OF HORUS

TODAY'S SYMBOL

FROM MYTH TO PRESCRIPTION PAD
In the Second Century, Galen used mystic symbols to impress patients. According to one theory, he borrowed from the Egyptian myth of the Eye of Horus *(top)* a symbol which has gradually evolved into today's familiar sign for "prescription." The myth tells how Horus, the falcon god, attacked his uncle to avenge his father's murder. In the fight, Horus' eye was torn, whereupon Thoth, patron god of physicians, miraculously healed it.

blood vessels some 3,300 years before the great William Harvey issued his epochal verdict on the circulatory system. Archeologists have turned up clay tablets providing instruction to medical students and hieroglyphs depicting the stomach, liver, windpipe, spleen, bladder and womb. Even the specialist flourished: the inscription on one doctor's tomb labels him "Guardian of the Royal Bowel Movement." The Egyptians' main source of anatomical education was the embalming process. In preparing their dead to be mummified, they had to remove the more perishable parts of the body, such as the brain, lungs and intestines, to preserve the rest. X-rays of mummies have confirmed the deftness of these manipulations.

With the golden age of Greece in the Fifth Century B.C., individual personalities began to leave a deeper imprint upon medical annals. The first was Hippocrates, forever memorialized through the *Hippocratic Corpus*—the early Western world's bible of medical practice. How much of this collection of writings was his own, and how much the work of other men, can only be conjectured. Its wealth of lore ranged from guidance on cranial surgery and cataract operations to such minutiae as the faint noise given off by the chest when pleurisy was present—a sound like "the rubbing of leather." Theoretical and philosophical counsel was also offered. The physician should consult his colleagues when in doubt; he had a duty to record, with utter honesty, his failures as well as successes in treatment; above all, without love for mankind, he could have no love for the art of healing. The Hippocratic code of ethics is still taken as a solemn oath at medical school commencement exercises today.

An ego and its impact

The influence of the next towering figure in the history of medicine, Galen, lasted for some 1,400 years, from the height of his own prestigious career as physician to the Roman Emperor Marcus Aurelius during the Second Century A.D., until the late Middle Ages—indeed beyond, for his descriptions of the larger muscles of the body appear in medical textbooks to this day. A Greek from Asia Minor, Galen had a personality which brooked neither self-doubt nor outside criticism. One unfortunate effect of this egotism was the perpetuation of a number of bad guesses and unsupported theories, among them that "spirits" existed in the bloodstream, and that there were 27 varieties of pulse, including the wavelike, wormlike and antlike. But for all his misconceptions, Galen gave far greater precision to existing knowledge of anatomy and physiology. His output of medical writing was phenomenal—more than 125 volumes, of which 83 still exist. They included treatises on the movement of muscles and on the intricate workings of nerves, and no fewer than 17 books on the uses of the various parts of the body.

With the restless new spirit of inquiry that began to pervade the West-

HEART   BONE   BRAIN

ANCIENT MEDICAL TEXT

An Egyptian papyrus of about 1700 B.C. indicates that physicians of the time knew something of anatomy. Hieroglyphs show such details as blood vessels emanating from the jug-shaped heart, although the symbol for bone is a structure like a coatrack. The symbols representing the brain include several phonetic signs. The papyrus dealt with injuries from head presumably to foot, although the surviving manuscript ends with the back.

ern world as the Renaissance approached, Galen's extended reign came to its end. His dethronement was bitterly fought; his teachings had both Church and academic blessing. Nevertheless, two men presumed to challenge his supremacy, and they prevailed.

Symbolic fire in a classroom

The first, Theophrastus Bombastus von Hohenheim, had all the swagger his middle name implied. Galen, at least, had acknowledged his debt to Hippocrates. This 16th Century Swiss healer deferred to no one. In fact, he is said to have chosen the name by which he is remembered—Paracelsus—to proclaim that he was superior even to Celsus, the great Roman encyclopedist. Paracelsus made a number of highly practical contributions to clinical medicine, among them one of the first studies of an occupational disease—the lung ailments of miners. But he left no less a legacy through a piece of brawling showmanship at the start of his teaching career at the University of Basel. Paracelsus launched his first lecture by setting fire to all the books by Galen he could find. In this symbolic act he expressed the abiding belief which he bequeathed to all students of anatomy since: study the patient, rather than the textbooks, if you are to learn about the body, for nothing supersedes the value of direct observation and experiment.

Andreas Vesalius of Belgium was only 13 when Paracelsus put Galen to the torch, but whether or not he heard of the deed he, too, concluded that Galen's ideas were imperfect. He studied medicine in Paris and then, at the improbable age of 23, was appointed a professor of anatomy at the University of Padua. By now dissection of the human cadaver—once banned as an impiety to the body—was no longer a rarity in medical classrooms. But those teachers who practiced it preferred merely to supply a running commentary, with pointer, as a hired barber-surgeon did the grubbing. Vesalius revolutionized this custom by performing his own dissections. He did them by the hundreds, and with such infinite pains that he was easily able to disprove many of Galen's assertions. After six years, he produced what has sometimes been called the greatest medical book ever written, *De Humani Corporis Fabrica* ("On the Fabric of the Human Body"). The first really accurate anatomy text, it was replete with minute detail and with brilliantly clear engravings by Stephen Calcar, a pupil of Titian. Some of them may be seen on pages 32 and 33.

After Paracelsus and Vesalius, the tempo of individual achievement in the field of anatomy began to step up. It was a feat of pure technology, however, that provided the next great threshold of exploration. This was the invention of the microscope. Thenceforth the study of anatomy became twofold. Gross anatomy dealt with what could be seen of the body with the unaided eye. Microscopic anatomy—now called histology—dealt

THE MAN WHO PUT AN END TO MEDICINE-BY-FIRE

AMBROISE PARE'S DISCOVERY

The tools shown below are medieval instruments for cauterizing gunshot wounds. During the battle of Turin in 1537, French surgeon Ambroise Paré *(above)* ran out of cauterizing oil. He began to dress wounds with simple dressings. Later he noticed that the patients responded to treatment more rapidly than did those whose wounds had been burned with hot oil. He vowed never again to cauterize wounded men.

with what had up to then been invisible and thus only speculative. Men could, at last, get to the nub of the matter: the cellular nature of all living things.

Simple magnifying lenses had been known as far back as the First Century A.D.; the Romans had used them for reading and for starting fires. But the microdimensional world around us could not begin to be fathomed until Hans and Zacharias Janssen, a father-and-son team of Dutch spectaclemakers, devised a microscope in 1590. As the first crude instruments gave way to finer models, they revealed an assortment of incredible wonders, most notably to the inquisitive eyes of Anton van Leeuwenhoek, a clerk for a dry-goods merchant of Delft. Fascinated by the potential of the microscope, Leeuwenhoek spent his off-duty hours scrutinizing through it any substance that came to hand—pond water, vinegar, milk, blood, bits of meat from between his teeth, scrapings from his palate. All teemed with what he called "animalcules." Some, it turned out, were common bacteria. But he also delved into the world of the cell, ascertaining not only its existence but also its variety of size and shape. He found, for instance, that the red cells of the blood were shaped like disks, while the cells lining the inside of the mouth were shaped like old-fashioned bathroom-floor tiles.

Foibles of a correspondent

Leeuwenhoek imperishably endeared himself to later researchers by writing down everything he observed. Over the course of 50 years— from 1673 to his death in 1723—he bombarded the new Royal Society in London with more than 200 letters about his findings. They were laced with Leeuwenhoek's crotchety asides about the inanities of his neighbors and the state of his own health. But the august members of the Society recognized the diamond in the rough. As they increasingly relished the acuity of his scientific observations, Leeuwenhoek's fame spread. The purveyor of textile sundries even put on a command performance for Czar Peter the Great of Russia, regaling that autocrat with a microscopic peek at the capillary circulation in an eel's tail.

Leeuwenhoek's studies of cells opened the door to a completely new concept of the makeup of all living organisms, including the human body. It did not dawn upon him, however, that the body might be made up *entirely* of cells. That remained to be confirmed a century later. In 1839 two Germans, Matthias Schleiden and Theodor Schwann, propounded the bedrock principle of our present understanding of the body: that all living matter is composed of cells basically similar in structure and function.

Subsequent studies of the cell—what it is, what it does and how it reproduces itself—have revealed it to be a fantastically complex world

A MAN OF MAGIC AND MEDICINE
Theophrastus Bombastus von Hohenheim, better known as Paracelsus, was the 16th Century Swiss physician who pioneered in the use of several modern medical techniques. Although he was also engrossed with the occult arts, Paracelsus is credited as the father of anesthesia; he wrote "Miners' Sickness," the first treatise on occupational diseases, and he insisted on cleanliness as a vital necessity for health.

in itself. For the purposes of this book, only certain fundamental facts about it need be stated here. One of the major wonders of the cell is the disparity between its minuteness and the prodigiousness of its activity. Each cell is so tiny that millions of them may be found in a half-inch cube of human body tissue. Yet each comprises an almost unimaginably busy chemical laboratory with a highly ordered division of labor.

A swarm of tiny specialists

The cell has two main parts: a nucleus, containing the genetic material deoxyribonucleic acid (DNA), and a surrounding semifluid cytoplasm. Bounding the cytoplasm is the cell membrane, which keeps the cell contents in and undesirable material out, yet permits passage of both proper nutrients and wastes. The nucleus—cell headquarters—governs the major activities of the cytoplasm; its finest hour, however, comes at reproduction time, when chromosomes containing DNA split. It is in the cytoplasm that the cell's day-to-day business is carried on. Each of its various components, or organelles, is a specialist of surpassing skill. One type breaks down the food given entry by the cell membrane and converts it into energy. Another provides the site for the synthesis of protein —along with reproduction, a major function of most cells. Another packages the manufactured protein for transport wherever needed in the body.

To operate efficiently, the cell thus requires specific help from the body as a whole: food to provide raw material for the release of energy, oxygen to help break down the food, water to transport inorganic substances like calcium and sodium. Once its needs are satisfied, the cell itself provides the intricate mechanism for maintaining the balance essential to keep it in kilter—in short, to keep the body alive and healthy.

In addition to the characteristics common to all cells, certain cells have specialized features and capabilities. Some—the special cells that form bone—collect calcium salts; these cells are locked together in solid chunks, immobile. By contrast, the white cells of the blood which fight off invading bacteria roam freely about the body. Other cells manufacture special chemicals for the body's use—the hormones produced in the endocrine glands, or the digestive enzymes poured into the intestine from the pancreas. Still other cells form the incredibly thin membranes in the lung or kidney that permit the filtering or exchange of dissolved body fuels and wastes.

According to their particular features and the jobs they are intended to do, cells combine to form different types of tissue: bone, muscle, blood, nerve tissue, connective tissue and epithelium. The cells that make up each of these are by no means identical, but belong together by reason of underlying similarities.

For example, the cells of bowel muscle are rounder and shorter than the long, spindly cells of leg muscle, yet both kinds contract forcefully when stimulated by a chemical or electrical impulse. The cells that make up bone tissue differ sufficiently to make brittle bone in one place and spongy, resilient cartilage in another, yet all store the salts which give bone its calcified structure. The loose network of cells that supports the fatty padding under the skin and the dense capsule of cells that holds the knee joint in place are both forms of connective tissue. All nerve cells, varied as they may be, receive and conduct electrochemical impulses. All blood cells, varied as they may be, float freely in a circulating fluid, plasma.

The most versatile cells are those of the various kinds of epithelium. Forming the body's external coating—the skin—epithelial cells protect things inside from things outside. They also form the lining of the mouth, stomach and bowel, the inner surface of blood vessels, and the membranes that permit the lungs to breathe and the kidneys to excrete. Other epithelial cells secrete a protective mucus to keep intestine, lungs and nasal passages from drying out. Still others manufacture powerful hormones that regulate the body's chemical reactions.

Interlock and overlap

The tissues comprise the structural materials of the body's organ systems. These, in turn, may be compared to a number of corporations with interlocking directorates. Indeed the interdependence of the organ systems has led to some disagreement over how many there are. The venerable *Gray's Anatomy*—which in 1959 celebrated a century of active service as a text for the medical student—lists 10 systems: nervous, digestive, respiratory, vascular, urogenital, endocrine, skeletal, muscular, joints and external covering. Other authorities categorize joints and bones together because they are so closely related, or separate the sense organs from the nervous system, or lump all the internal organs—respiratory, digestive, endocrine and urogenital—under the resounding title of splanchnological system.

Far more important than their labels is the fact that the systems interact; the breakdown of one can damage or destroy the others. Ideally, of course, all systems would do their jobs perfectly all the time. Unfortunately, nature permits no such perfection. All of them suffer from malfunctions at one point or another. The wonder is that breakdowns are the exception rather than the rule.

Within the healthy body itself there is no absolute criterion for "normal." Variations occur not only between individuals, but within the individual himself, sometimes from hour to hour, depending on his activity at the time. Doctors privately joke that even a baboon could get through medical school if he learned to say, with enough profundity, "It varies." One of the practitioner's major headaches is to determine whether a pa-

圖五十九——仿明版古圖（五）

CHINESE MEDICAL CHART

This Ming Dynasty (14th to 17th Century) drawing is, according to the archaic Chinese characters to its right, a chart for curing kidney ailments. The vertical line plotted on the patient was believed to relate to the kidney; the cure consisted of jabbing it with needles in the 27 places indicated. Called "acupuncture" (from *acus*, or needle), the art of pricking the ill along lines plotted centuries ago is still practiced in the Orient and Europe.

tient's condition reflects an actual illness or merely a variation within a broad range of normal. The breadth of this range may be indicated by a few statistics. The weight of the healthy heart is considered to be anywhere between 240 and 360 grams; the weight of the healthy liver, between 1,200 and 1,700 grams; the level of sugar in the blood, between 80 and 120 milligrams.

Aside from the range of normal, another remarkable aspect of the body is its range of strength and weakness. It can survive in blast-furnace desert heat by adjusting its built-in heating system, yet an internal temperature eight degrees above the normal range of 97 to 99 degrees may destroy vital nervous tissue. A man can draw enough food from stored fat to stay alive for weeks (provided he has water), but would die in about five minutes if the oxygen supply to all his cells were cut off by a failure in breathing. An Olympics champion has lifted as much as 1,212½ pounds, deadweight, yet a vacation-bound executive lifting a heavy suitcase may bring on the agony of a "slipped disk" in his spine.

The human body has no corner on such strengths and weaknesses; they are shared by all mammals. The uniqueness of man's strength, perhaps, lies in the fact that his body was not built for just one or two specialized purposes, but is marvelously adaptable. That he is so unspecialized, indeed, may account for his dominance among the species on this planet.

Changing Views of the Body

From prehistoric times until the mid-16th Century, when the findings of the physician-teacher Vesalius established the principle of firsthand observation, the body was seen less as a biological organization than as a house for the spirit. The scientific study of the human body is in fact a relatively recent development. The ancients rooted their studies in the butchery of animals at the altar and in the kitchen, but investigations were fettered by superstition, religion and tradition. Nevertheless, the exigencies of everyday life—on the battlefield, in the sickroom—demanded that wounds be healed and ailments cured. Thus, driven by the need to doctor diseases of every kind, men learned the chief parts of the body, devised names for them and evolved theories to account for their miraculous operation. These theories, although ultimately replaced by more useful concepts, were defended with a faith which it took a Renaissance to dislodge.

A 15TH CENTURY ANATOMY CLASS
Perched in a pulpit, a red-robed professor of anatomy delivers the gospel according to Galen, a Second Century Greek physician whose theories, based on the observation of animals, animated medicine for 1,400 years. An assistant *(far right)* points out parts of the body while a barber-surgeon dissects the cadaver. If actual observations conflicted with Galen, they were discarded.

Primitive Surgeons of the Skull

Guided by empirical observations and magical beliefs but armed with little more than sharpened flints, Cro-Magnon "surgeons" learned about the body while treating diseases, setting broken bones and caring for wounds.

The most spectacular practice of the era was trephination, the surgical exposure of the brain to permit the flight of "spirits" from the heads of persons suffering from fractures, epilepsy, migraine, melancholia and paralysis. These trephined skulls have been found among the remains of primitive peoples around the world.

The operation consisted of opening the scalp to uncover the cranial bone, cutting out a round *(above)* or square piece of bone *(right)*, cleansing and dressing the opening and, finally, replacing the scalp flap. Since the skull is generally insensitive to pain, especially on the top, no drugs were needed to anesthetize the patient during the operation—which took anywhere from 30 minutes to several hours to perform. The presence of new bone growth around the incisions *(above right)* indicates the remarkable fact that about half the patients survived.

AN ORNATE SURGICAL KNIFE
The sculpted scene on the handle-tip of this Peruvian *tumi,* or trephining knife, shows how the operation was performed. The patient is held as the surgeon scrapes through to the bone with his bronze scalpel. This instrument was designed for cross-hatched cuts like those shown below.

VICTIM AND SURVIVOR
Two Paleolithic skulls *(above)* from Denmark reveal healed and unhealed trephined openings. The skull at right shows how new growth began at the edges and filled in much of the opening. The skull at left indicates the patient died before the bone had time to grow again.

A PAIR OF WINDOWS ON THE BRAIN
Cross-hatch trephination, achieved by intersecting straight cuts *(right),* was performed in Peru some 12,000 years ago. Survival depended on the location of the boring. If it touched on the sagittal suture—the midline at the top of the skull—fatal hemorrhaging often occurred.

A Religious Minor Contribution

Egyptian religion at the time of the early pharaohs might have served as a fruitful source of anatomical knowledge, for through the sacred ritual of embalming the dead the Egyptians evolved an extensive medical vocabulary and wrote the first medical texts. However, embalming was a process of preservation, not a discipline for studying the structure of the body. As a consequence, organs were carelessly removed and dissections for the sake of knowledge were not performed. Nevertheless, the effects —if not the causes—of injuries and diseases were noted, and experiments in surgery and pharmacy were conducted. Egyptian physicians learned to use splints and bandages with skill, and their remedies became famous.

AN ANTIDOTE FOR POISONS
A granite statue of the healer-priest Dje-Mer, sculpted in 320 B.C. *(above),* is covered with magical inscriptions to combat scorpion stings and snake bites. Water poured over the statue accumulated in a small depression at its base and, when drunk, supposedly effected a cure.

PREPARATIONS FOR A JOURNEY
This mummification scene *(opposite)* on the coffin of the priest Zed-Bastet-Fesanch shows (reading from bottom to top) two priests cleansing and anointing the body; a procession led by the jackal-headed god Anubis, at the bier; Anubis mummifying the body and placing it on another bier above jars containing entrails; offerings at the shrine where the entrails are kept.

A UNIVERSAL EGYPTIAN REMEDY
In this painted relief, a tiny physician dispenses beer to his lordly patient. Beer was frequently used to administer drugs orally. And the lees, or dregs, of beer were themselves important emollients prescribed for digestive disorders and for boils. In our own time, it has been discovered that these dregs are a source of vitamin B and a number of valuable antibiotic substances.

CURE FOR A WOUNDED HERO

A fresco from Pompeii depicts a scene from Virgil's *Aeneid* in which the hero Aeneas, supported by his spear and his son Julius, is treated by the physician, Iapix. Venus, Aeneas' mother-goddess, appears with a medicinal herb which will stop the flow of blood and ease the pain.

An Enlightened Look at the Body

The physician-naturalists of ancient Greece viewed the human body as a subject for dispassionate study unconditioned by superstitions. Clinical observations led physicians like Hippocrates in the Fifth Century B.C. to conceive of the body as a grouping of interrelated parts, and illness as a malfunction of one or more of these parts. Such precedents paved the way for the great anatomical researches of Galen, a Second Century Greek physician who practiced in Rome. Galen's work describing his examinations of human bones and animal viscera became the bible of anatomists for the next 1,400 years.

CLUES IN AN ANIMAL'S ENTRAILS
This Etruscan bronze model of a sheep's liver from the Third Century B.C. is inscribed with the names of 47 divinities believed to cause sickness in humans. Discovering real or imagined peculiarities in livers of sacrificed sheep was a popular Roman diagnostic technique.

AN ANCIENT DOCTOR'S TOOLS
Roman surgical instruments include *(from left to right)* a scalpel handle for steel blades, an arrowhead retractor, forceps, another retractor, a surgical saw, a hook for tissue excision, a scalpel, a spoon for warming salves and another scalpel handle. In the center is a bleeding cup.

Fanciful Figures in Medieval Anatomy

During the Middle Ages, knowledge of anatomy and the various body systems was derived almost exclusively from the works of Galen, which were not illustrated. The quartet of bizarre bodies below, for example, was appended to a 13th Century English medical manuscript and was thought to represent Galen's ideas of the body's inner structures. These primitive drawings may have been inspired by an Arabic book, like the one opposite, or they may have been the renderings of an imaginative artist. In either case, the text itself was rooted in Galen. He originally wrote in Greek and, over the centuries, was translated from Greek to Arabic and, from the 11th Century on, from Arabic into Latin.

Despite the misconceptions of the original and the embellishments of countless translators, few dared to question Galen's authority. Even when human dissections began to gain acceptance, their sole intention was to verify Galen's observations. In the gross distortions below, undersized lungs are joined, upper ribs are completely absent, the nervous system does not include the brain and the esophagus leads to the heart.

Drawings from this medieval manuscript show (from left to right) the major human organs plus the muscular system; the skeletal

AN ARAB TREATISE

The *Canon of Medicine* by ibn Sina, or Avicenna (980-1037), the greatest Arab physician-scholar of his day, is based on Arabic versions of Galen. On the right-hand page is a drawing of Avicenna lecturing to students; on the left, a rendering of the body similar to those shown below. Avicenna's anatomical works were the most widely read in Europe in the late Middle Ages.

structure; the nervous and circulatory systems. The crude sketches failed to emphasize Galen's belief in the importance of the liver.

TREPHINATION

PALPATING

Medieval Sense and Nonsense

To the doctors of the Middle Ages, common sense in dealing with the human body was a quality that usually yielded to uncommon faith and a reliance on tradition. Consequently, they often employed accurate diagnostic techniques for ailments that they then treated with irrelevant, even fatal, cures based on ancient theories.

For example, physicians like those shown here were able to arrive at a primitive estimate of body temperatures and of pathological changes in the spleen and liver by palpating, or feeling, the chest and abdomen (*center*). Or, in taking the pulse (*right*), they could feel the arterial pressure and the flexibility of the blood-vessel walls. But because they believed that an imbalance of four body fluids, called humors, led to disease, these physicians frequently ended up applying dangerous remedies. Two of them, bloodletting and trephination (*far left*), had originated in antiquity.

DIAGNOSIS AND "CURE"
Drawings from the pages of an illuminated manuscript on anatomy written by Guido da Vigevano, a physician to Philip VI of France in the middle 1300s, show an operation to open the skull and two types of physical examinations. By this time the Church had prohibited clergymen from practicing medicine, for it took up too much of their time. Thus, medicine was secularized; the practice passed to barber-surgeons and the theory to university-trained physicians.

PULSE-TAKING

A Spate of Bizarre Remedies

The apothecaries of the Middle Ages and Renaissance viewed the human body as an experimental laboratory in which almost any substance could be tested in the hope of finding cures for almost everything. In a very real sense, their customers were the guinea pigs of the day, and often failed to survive the treatment.

As late as the 16th Century, European pharmacy was still based on the work of Dioscorides. A Greek surgeon and naturalist of the First Century, he compiled the knowledge of plant remedies handed down by the Egyptians, Greeks and Romans. His and other compilations were known as herbals. They included both sound suggestions, such as poppy juice to kill pain (poppies are now known to contain the narcotic, opium), and seemingly inane ideas, such as the use of strawberry roots for mad-dog bites and oats for impetigo. Minerals too were used to assault the ailing body, as were animal fat, marrow and bones. Even crocodile blood was recommended—for failing eyesight.

Often apothecaries diagnosed diseases to sell a certain plant cure. Actually they had little knowledge of medicine. Indeed, until the 14th Century, apothecaries were grocers who carried medicines as a sideline.

AZTEC PLANT TO TREAT PELVIC DISORDERS

AZTEC MEDICINAL PLANT DESCRIBED IN 1552

AN APOTHECARY SHOP
An illumination from a 13th Century manuscript shows an apothecary and customer. Apothecaries gathered herbs and prepared thousands of supposed remedies. Sometimes one prescription contained a hundred or more drugs, some of which came from as far away as the New World.

The illuminations in a 1505 prayer book show roses, used for eye and heart disorders, and lilies, used for burns.

Harassing the Body's Humors

Since the cause of disease was considered to be morbid influences on the body's humors—blood, phlegm, black bile and yellow bile—it followed that many illnesses could be diagnosed by examining the body's discharges and treated by allowing the ostensibly infected fluids to escape. By the end of the 15th Century this logic had made uroscopy the chief form of diagnosis and elevated bloodletting to the status of a universal treatment. So fashionable were they that physicians amassed fortunes in their application.

Doctors like those at left would examine vials of urine to determine its color, odor, density and content. The sediment in a urine sample was thought to be made up of four layers, each of which corresponded to a region of the body. Cloudiness of the top layer, for example, was supposed to indicate a disease of the head; of the bottom layer, a bladder disorder, and so on. The usual cure for these and other ailments was bleeding. Much controversy was generated around how much blood should be taken, when, and how near or distant from the affliction the incision should be made. Thus the Italian poet Petrarch could quote Pliny condemning physicians who, "to make a name for themselves through some novelty . . . traffic with our lives."

THE PHYSICIANS' OFFICE
An illuminated drawing from a manuscript executed at Bruges around 1482 depicts a pair of patients waiting for treatment outside an office shared by two physicians. Inside, the richly clad colleagues are taking blood from one patient's arm and examining the urine of another. Frequently leeches were used instead of a knife to "suck" humors from a diseased area.

SOLVITVR OMNE DECVS
LETO, NIVEOS'QVE
PER ARTVS
IT STYGIVS COLOR, ET
FORMAE POPVLA·
TVR HONO·
RES.

PORTRAIT OF VESALIUS BY CALCAR

The Beginning of Modern Medicine

In 1543, the year the Flemish-born anatomist Andreas Vesalius first published his controversial epic, *De Humani Corporis Fabrica*, the dictum, "It is more right to err with Galen than be right with others," was finally and irrevocably discredited. Vesalius, who taught at the University of Padua, was only 29 years old when he introduced a systematic anatomy founded not on faith and analogies from animal anatomy but on studies of original dissections of the human cadaver.

De Fabrica, which is still a basically accurate guide to bones and joints, muscles, the vascular and nervous systems, viscera, heart, lungs and brain, was exquisitely illustrated by Stephen Calcar, two of whose woodcuts are reproduced on these pages.

A THOUGHTFUL SKELETON
A woodcut *(left)* from *De Fabrica* shows a skeleton meditating over a skull. Posing these figures in lifelike positions was characteristic of Calcar, who worked under Vesalius' direct supervision.

A FLAYED BODY
A figure from *De Fabrica* looks out over authentic countryside near Padua. If the backgrounds to these muscle illustrations are placed in a sequence, they will form a continuous landscape.

VNDECIMA
MVSCVLO,
RVM TA-
BVLA.

2
Hallmarks of Individual Identity

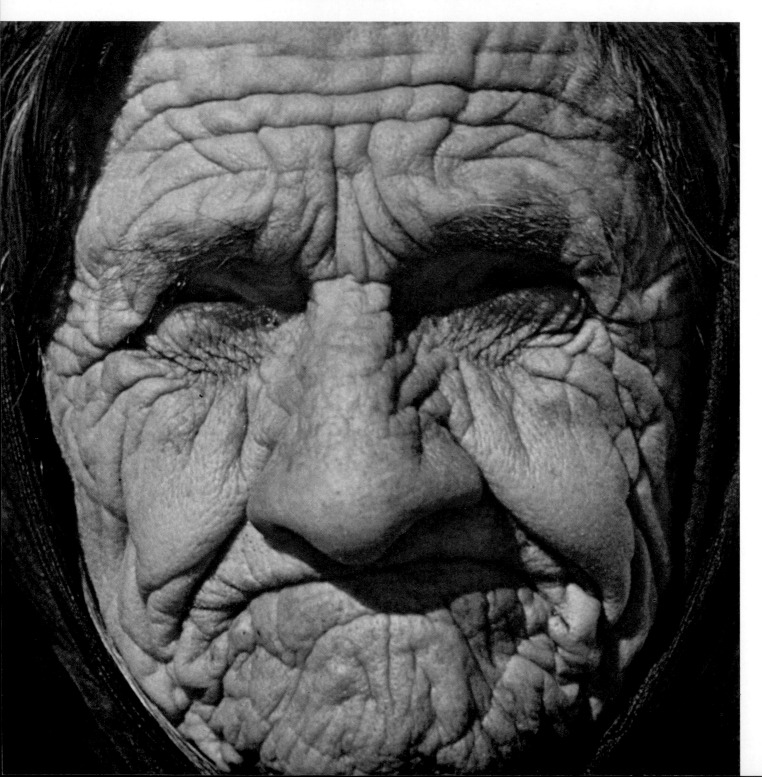

AN ESTIMATED THREE BILLION HUMAN BEINGS inhabit the earth, yet not one exactly duplicates another. This is a fact most people would find difficult to believe. Occidentals often cannot distinguish between Orientals, an inability which Orientals reciprocate. Even within one's own race, the conviction persists that each man has his exact double, somehow, somewhere.

Strong resemblances of face and figure do, indeed, exist. Often they are striking enough to provide a tyrant or other potential human target with an effective stand-in. In one historic case in World War II records, an Australian actor posing as Field Marshal Montgomery visited North Africa before D-Day and filled the part so well that German agents promptly discounted the imminence of a Normandy invasion. Had the British military leader and his impersonator stood side by side, however, the differences between them would have been easily apparent. Even so-called identical twins have their dissimilarities, however minute.

One of the most remarkable features of the human body, in short, is its individuality of appearance. The odds would seem to be overwhelmingly against such uniqueness. The relatively few major components of the human exterior should, in theory at least, diversify in only limited ways. On the contrary, they form an infinity of variations. Each man's shell is his own personal ensign, clearly setting him apart from any other human being in the present or past.

Heredity, environment and certain glands within the body all do their share in fashioning the physical differences which we present to the world. The influence of these factors is so intertwined that no scientist has yet been able to say, with certainty, where one leaves off and the other begins. The size of the body, for example, is basically determined by skeletal structure, which is largely a family and racial inheritance. But size may also be vitally affected by environmental conditions, notably those which provide adequate nutrition and freedom from disease, and by a hormone called somatotropin. This substance, named from the Greek for "body-nourishing," is secreted by the front lobe of the pituitary gland, at the base of the skull, and is essential for normal growth. A shortage of somatotropin during youth, when bones have not yet matured, will stunt the body.

Perhaps the most curious fact about the human exterior is the tendency of most people to dissociate it from matters of bodily health, to regard it as simply a front behind which the business of well-being is independently conducted. More often than not, their sole concern with this façade is to adorn it. Indeed, statistics show that Americans spend more for cosmetics each year than the Federal Government's National Institutes of Health provide in grants for medical research. In 1961, for example, Americans lavished $121,680,000 on lipsticks alone, $127,600,000 on face

THE STAMP OF ORIGINALITY
Laced with wrinkles and sagging with folds of flesh, the face of this Tennessee woman, age 77, would seem at first glance to be indistinguishable from those of legions of other oldsters. But as with each individual, her toilworn features reflect a particular confluence of hereditary and environmental factors that bestows the gift of uniqueness upon every human exterior.

creams and $74,440,000 on hair-coloring preparations. They also paid out $337,010,000 for reducing aids.

(The scope of human vanity is, of course, far from a new story. In 1770 an Englishman who may have been soured by personal experience introduced into Parliament a bill which revealed the wide range of surface attractions employed by the women of the realm. He proposed to pin a witchcraft charge on any of them—"of whatever age, rank, profession, or degree, whether virgins, maids, or widows"—who lured one of His Majesty's subjects into matrimony by the use of "scents, paints, cosmetic washes, artificial teeth, false hair, Spanish wool, iron stays, hoops, high heeled shoes, bolstered hips.")

Signals from a showcase

While no doctor would dispute the importance of a reasonable amount of pride in self-appearance, the outer covering of the body—the so-called cutaneous system—serves a number of purposes far more sober than that of mere showcase. It is, to begin with, the most obvious indicator of an individual's general condition. Among the more apparent indexes are flabbiness, an overabundance of fat or a notable scarcity of it. But to the physician's practiced eye there are many other signs of health, or lack of it, in the skin and its related structures, the hair and nails. The skin alone provides many warning signals. Its texture may reflect nutritional deficiency or glandular malfunction. A flush may indicate the presence of fever. A rash or other eruption may herald many common infections. Coarsening and wrinkling furnish clues to aging.

The skin, however, not only mirrors but also actively contributes to bodily health. It is as much a vital organ as the heart, liver or lungs and, like each of them, has its own special responsibilities:

• It is a nearly waterproof container, enclosing the body's content, 60 per cent of which is fluid, and preventing it from drying out.
• It is a receptor, housing nerve endings which receive sensory stimuli from the environment.
• It is both a radiator and retainer of heat, helping regulate the body's temperature.
• It is a barrier, guarding the body against external injury and disease-causing organisms.

The skin is endowed with double insurance against a breakdown in these crucial functions. First, it has a remarkable ability to regenerate itself. When pierced by a wound, or otherwise damaged, it responds with an immediate proliferation of new skin cells; so thoroughgoing is the healing process that when, for example, a fingertip is injured, even the fingerprint whorls will be restored to their previous pattern. Second, the skin can respond well to an emergency created by damage so severe

PLAIN ARCH

TENTED ARCH

RADIAL LOOP (RIGHT HAND)

ULNAR LOOP (RIGHT HAND)

PLAIN WHORL

that the full thickness of the skin is destroyed, as in the case of a third-degree burn. In most cases it proves strikingly receptive to a graft of a thin layer of skin from another part of the body. Usually applied to the burned area in little squares of postage-stamp size, the transplanted skin eventually adapts to its new site, growing more skin out from its edges until the patches all meet. Meanwhile, skin on the donor site regenerates on its own.

The skin is at no point more than about three-sixteenths of an inch thick—testimony enough to the truth of the term "skin-deep." But for all its shallowness, it is a marvelously intricate structure, composed of layer upon layer—each with its own reason for being.

The epidermis, or outer part of the skin, is composed of two to four layers, depending on the particular area of the body; the dermis, or inner part of the skin, has two layers. One of the primary functions of the epidermis is to guard the body against abrasive and destructive forces in the surrounding environment, and to do so it invokes a variety of stratagems. To shield the cornea of the eye, it provides the delicate outer covering of the eyelid. To protect the tips of the fingers and toes, it produces keratin, the substance of which nails are made. To counter wear and tear on pressure points such as the palms of the hands and soles of the feet, it thickens into callus. As a protector, the epidermis is highly adaptable: its thickness over the soles of the feet may be as much as a sixteenth of an inch, over the eyelid less than two thousandths of an inch.

The versatile epidermis

To fit other purposes which it serves, the epidermis assumes diverse guises and shapes. Over the eye, to permit the free entry of light to the retina, it forms a sort of transparent windshield. On the fingertips, to provide the necessary traction and grip, it forms tiny ridges similar to the treads on an automobile tire. Over the knuckles, elbows and knees it is pleated, to allow flexibility of the joints.

The epidermis is self-renewing. Cells produced in its bottom layer, the *stratum germinativum,* constantly push upward to replace the dead and dying cells topside. These surface cells form a horny, scaly layer of their own; a brisk toweling of the skin is enough to rub off a fair sampling of it.

In addition to its function as cell-restorer, the *stratum germinativum* plays another key role, one which has caused a considerable share of the world's woes. It is the main home of the melanocytes, a variety of cell which produces melanin, the pigment responsible for skin color; other melanocytes, located in the hair and the iris of the eye, produce the melanin which decides hair and eye color. There are no differences among the races of mankind in the number of melanocytes their skins contain. What causes the difference in color is the way that the melanin is dis-

CENTRAL POCKET LOOP

DOUBLE LOOP

ACCIDENTAL

tributed in the skin and the quantity of it that is produced. The melanocytes of the fair-complexioned, for example, contain only a few granules of melanin, while those of the dark-skinned teem with it; the melanocytes of the brown-eyed contain more melanin than those of the blue-eyed; in the hair, graying signals a stoppage in melanin production.

The scrawny or the stout

Beneath the *stratum germinativum* and its hubbub of cellular activity lie the layers of the dermis, and below the dermis lies a webbing of fibrous tissue, the subcutaneous fascia (literally, "bundles under the skin"), which is the last barrier between the skin and the body's interior. Within these areas are contained the nerve endings, the smallest blood vessels, the roots of the hair, the sweat glands, the sebaceous, or oil-producing, glands which help give the skin its softness and pliancy, and the globules of fat which, depending on the amount accumulated, make us appear scrawny, sylphlike or stout.

Even as the outer part of the skin provides external protection for the body, the inner part also has its specialized functions to perform. Although widely varied in nature, each of these is capable of adding to or detracting from our physical enjoyment of life.

One such function is to receive sensory stimuli and to transmit them to the brain as nerve impulses. These stimuli are set off by pressure, changes in temperature and tissue damage, and produce sensations of touch, warmth, cold and pain, as well as an awareness of comfort or discomfort. Some anthropologists and psychiatrists, indeed, regard the skin as an important factor in the foundation of a happy family relationship. They hold that when an infant is bathed and cuddled, the skin becomes the means by which he first receives affection and a sense of security from his mother.

The skin transmits sensory impulses more readily from some areas than others, depending upon the abundance of nerve fibers in a particular area. On the face, the soles of the feet and the palms of the hands, these fibers are densely packed within the skin. This explains, for example, why facial pain is often more accurately localized than pain elsewhere in the body. It also explains why blind people can read Braille through their fingertips.

Another essential function of the skin is to help put a brake on any tendency of the body to grow too hot or too cold. The main regulator of bodily temperature is located in a part of the brain known as the hypothalamus. Its collaboration with the skin is close and continuing. The hypothalamus has two thermostats, one to register a rise and one to register a drop in normal body temperatures. At a signal from one thermostat, indicating overheating of the body, circulation of the blood to the

SUNTAN AND FRECKLES

The skin of every race (except in the case of albinos) produces a certain amount of melanin, a dark pigment which absorbs ultraviolet light. Cells called melanocytes produce this pigment at rates which speed up on exposure to sunlight. When they speed up, the skin darkens—hence the sunbather's tan. If the sunbather's enthusiasm outstrips the rate at which his melanocytes can produce pigment, excess ultraviolet light results in a mysterious release of a chemical in the skin, causing blood vessels to swell and the skin to become red and sore. Active melanocytes surrounded by less active melanocytes produce the islands of pigment known as freckles.

MELANIN GRANULES

MELANOCYTE

AVERAGE SKIN

BLOOD VESSEL

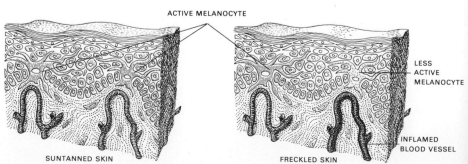

ACTIVE MELANOCYTE

LESS ACTIVE MELANOCYTE

INFLAMED BLOOD VESSEL

SUNTANNED SKIN

FRECKLED SKIN

skin is stepped up, and the heat from the internal organs is carried into a network of small blood vessels just beneath the skin, there to be dissipated. Simultaneously the same thermostat spurs the activity of the sweat glands. Millions of these glands lie coiled deep in the dermis and subcutaneous tissue; they open onto the skin surface through the pores. The increased perspiration which results is evaporated on contact with moving air outside the body; this provides efficient cooling-off.

Conversely, when the other thermostat in the hypothalamus signals a drop in body temperature, the flow of blood to the skin slows down and the sweat glands produce less. As the outward rush of blood dwindles, the skin itself and the layer of fat beneath it function as insulators to conserve whatever bodily heat there is. One physiologist has estimated that a body swathed in clothes is only a quarter more efficiently insulated than a body that is stark-naked. The natural insulation is even better in the case of the female body, with its naturally more abundant deposits of fat—an estimated 28 per cent of the body's mass as opposed to a mere 18 per cent for the male.

Despite its virtue as a guardian of bodily heat, fat is seldom appreciated; its possessor is more often busy maligning it. Yet fatty tissue serves more than one useful and admirable purpose. It furnishes an emergency food supply in the event that normal sustenance is stopped. It provides a shock absorber that prevents injury to bone except at relatively exposed areas such as the skull, the collarbone or the shin. It helps form the body's pleasantly rounded contours. Where fat should cease to be welcome is the point at which it becomes excess.

A riddle of excess

The question of what constitutes excess, however, has no pat answer. A great deal depends on the size of the skeletal structure to which the fat is attached, and the variations in this structure are countless. One homespun measure that is sometimes applied is to grasp, between the thumb and forefinger, the skin at the side of the body just above the waistline. If the thickness is more than an inch, the fat is presumed to be excessive. But this particular rule of thumb is far from infallible. Many doctors, when a patient poses the problem of the degree of surplus, present him with a statistical table of average weights to ponder and leave the rest to his conscience and his mirror.

Fat and other controllable features of the human exterior, along with those fashioned by heredity and by the glands, produce the illimitable combinations which stamp each man as unique. Perennially and persistently, his body defies convenient pigeonholing. Nowhere within the frame of human existence is individualism more rampant.

At best, attempts to place people in categories produce broad generalizations, and even to these the exceptions are legion. Efforts along this line have been undertaken in almost every century since civilization began. Some were born simply of a passion for orderliness. Some were made with a view to determining possible relationships between physique and various illnesses and diseases, and indeed between the outer and inner self. The great Aristotle, for example, was convinced that a man's character could be read merely by the shape of his nose.

One system for sorting people into distinguishable types has been to classify them according to race. This approach has proved as scientifically inconclusive as it has been socially and politically explosive. One of the first attempts of this nature was made in the late 18th Century by a young German zoologist, Johann Friedrich Blumenbach, who is generally regarded as the founder of modern anthropology, the broad study of mankind. Blumenbach used only one physical criterion: skin color. Depending on whether the individual's skin was white, yellow, black, red or brown, he was classified respectively as a member of the Caucasian, Mongolian, Ethiopian, American or Malayan race.

In time, as successive classifiers warmed to their task, they not only added variations of these basic skin colors but also set forth a number of other external characteristics that might make man recognizable by race, and by subrace as well. Among these were the conformation of skeletal structure, the shape of the face, the shape of the nose, the degree of protrusion of the jaw, the texture of the hair and the extent of its distribution on the body.

Badges of identity

Out of all this study came multitudinous data designed to pin a permanent badge of racial identification on every inhabitant of the planet. Those classified as Mongoloids, for example, were likely to have straight black hair, broad, flat faces with low noses and fatty eyelids, and little growth of hair on the face or body. Negroids were likely to have deep pigmentation, woolly hair, low noses, jutting lips and projecting jaws. Caucasoids were likely to have long noses, generally lighter skins and much body hair. Among the Caucasoids, a number of variations of skeletal structure was duly noted: the Scandinavians, for example, were likely to have long, slender bones, the people of Central and Southern Europe short, bulky bones.

A more precise approach to the problem of bringing order out of human diversity has been to set up classifications of physique, a practice known as somatotyping. This system was used by none other than Hippocrates himself. He saw man as belonging to one of two main types: the short and fat, which he labeled apoplectic, or the tall and slender, which he labeled phthisic ("wasting away").

INFANT ABOUT SIX MONTHS OLD

ADULT ABOUT 30 YEARS OLD

ADULT ABOUT 80 YEARS OLD

THE AGING OF A FACE

Aging is most apparent in the face, not only because of its effects on skin but because of skull changes as well. The drawings above illustrate the process. The infant's jaws are small compared to his braincase, still with the so-called "soft spot" on top; his chipmunklike jowls are layers of fat called sucking cushions. As he matures, his jaws lengthen and his braincase becomes dome-shaped. By advanced age, degeneration of bone has shrunk the skull, and wear on the teeth—or loss of teeth— shortens the distance from nose to chin. Skin and muscles atrophy and the face sags in wrinkles upon the diminished skull.

More than 2,000 years after Hippocrates, the physical anthropologists dusted off his idea and embellished it, with the aid of techniques supplied by the new subsciences of anthropometry, or body measurement, and anthroposcopy, the visual study and comparison of bodily variations.

By far the most widely known method of somatotyping devised up to now is the creation of an American psychologist, William H. Sheldon. First revealed in 1940, Sheldon's classifications sorted humanity into endomorph, mesomorph and ectomorph. These labels he derived from the three layers of cells in the developing embryo—the endoderm, an inner layer predominating in the digestive organs, the mesoderm, a middle layer predominating in the skeleton, muscles and circulation, and the ectoderm, an outer layer predominating in the skin, hair, nails and nervous system. Sheldon propounded the theory that according to the ways these layers developed, in each person one layer prevailed. Thus his endomorph was a visceral type, round and fat in head and body, with weak limbs, small extremities and large internal organs. His mesomorph was Herculean, big-boned, with a square, hard body, prominent chest, large hands and feet and well-developed limbs. His ectomorph was thin, weedy, delicate and linear in body, with a highly developed nervous system.

According to whether the gut, the body itself, or the brain appeared to rule, Sheldon suggested three correlated types of temperament: viscerotonic (sociable and comfortable), somatotonic (aggressive and noisy) and cerebrotonic (introverted and inhibited). He cautioned, however, that these correlations were only rough and, in an expert's obeisance to individuality, he also noted that in any event few persons perfectly embodied any of the three types he had described. As in other attempts at classification, there are a great many recalcitrant individuals who refuse to fit into the prescribed slots.

The physique of the future

There are some anthropologists venturesome enough to predict the look of man 10,000 years, half a million years or even a million years hence. Although to the layman this variety of prophesying may seem no more than a parlor guessing game, the scientists show a substantial amount of unanimity on the human physique of the future and offer sound reasons for their views.

• Hair, traditionally the crowning glory of the female and a focus of anxiety of the male, may diminish almost to the vanishing point. Even now hair is a relatively vestigial feature; among the primates, man has the least of it, although it continues to provide some protection (as in the eyebrows and eyelashes), some cushioning against injury, a shield against overheating or overcooling of the head, and sensory warning

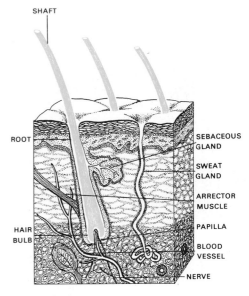

SHAFT

ROOT

SEBACEOUS GLAND

SWEAT GLAND

ARRECTOR MUSCLE

PAPILLA

HAIR BULB

BLOOD VESSEL

NERVE

THE HUMAN HAIR
Virtually the entire human skin is covered with hair, though much of it is too fine to be visible. It is relatively vestigial compared to the hair covering of other primates, but it still serves a purpose, if only by being highly sensitive to touch. The part above the skin is the shaft; below the surface is the root. The root, bulbous at the bottom, is enclosed in a follicle surrounded by fine nerves. Connective tissue at the base of the bulb (the papilla) contains other nerve fibers, capillaries and occasional pigment cells. Sebaceous glands secrete lubricating oil, and the arrector muscles can literally make hair stand on end.

against the imminence of an insect bite. As civilization has added its comforts of clothing and shelter against cold, a heavy coating of hair, either on the body or head, has become less essential.

• Future man may have not only a hairless dome but also a larger one, to allow room for a bigger brain.

• Jaws may be smaller, thanks to softer food to chew. One sign of this change is the increasing failure even today of our third molars—wisdom teeth—to show up.

• With smaller jaws, the nose may look larger.

• Unless we somehow return to the strenuous life, the body may be less muscular and the bones less massive. Legs may become more sticklike with less use, and the small toe may entirely disappear.

As against this somewhat unpalatable picture of a high-domed, top-heavy, spindly-legged creature, there are those in the scientific community who argue that thanks to man's increasing control over the internal chemistry of his body, as well as over changes in his external environment, the human exterior in ages to come will look pretty much the same as it does today.

Whatever school of thought prevails, on one point there is agreement. Each man will somehow manage to retain the stubbornly unique arrangement of features that sets him apart from his neighbor.

An Atlas of the Anatomy

In the 400 years that have passed since Vesalius launched a revolution in medical science with the accuracy and detail of his anatomical opus, *De Humani Corporis Fabrica*, the firsthand study of the dissected body has become the foundation of man's knowledge of the human organism. Anatomy offers both an over-all look at the body's structure and a first glimpse of how it functions. To the uninitiated, the anatomy appears to be a conglomeration of bone and muscle, oddly shaped internal organs, and networks of blood vessels and nerves. But generations of anatomists have organized the many parts of the body into separate anatomical systems and named their parts. Echoing Vesalius' book, which set figures against miniature landscapes, the pictures on these pages show these systems—skeletal, muscular, circulatory, nervous and visceral—in the form of shadowy athletes against fanciful backgrounds; the parts bear their scientific names.

A HOUSE FOR THE BRAIN

A ghostly ensemble of 22 bones and toothy grin, the human skull *(opposite)* consists of a rigid cranium in which the sensitive brain is safely stored, and the facial skeleton with its movable lower jaw, which enables man to talk and eat. The tiny holes, or foramens, on the forehead, cheekbone and jaw are the orifices through which nerves pass to and from the brain and the skin.

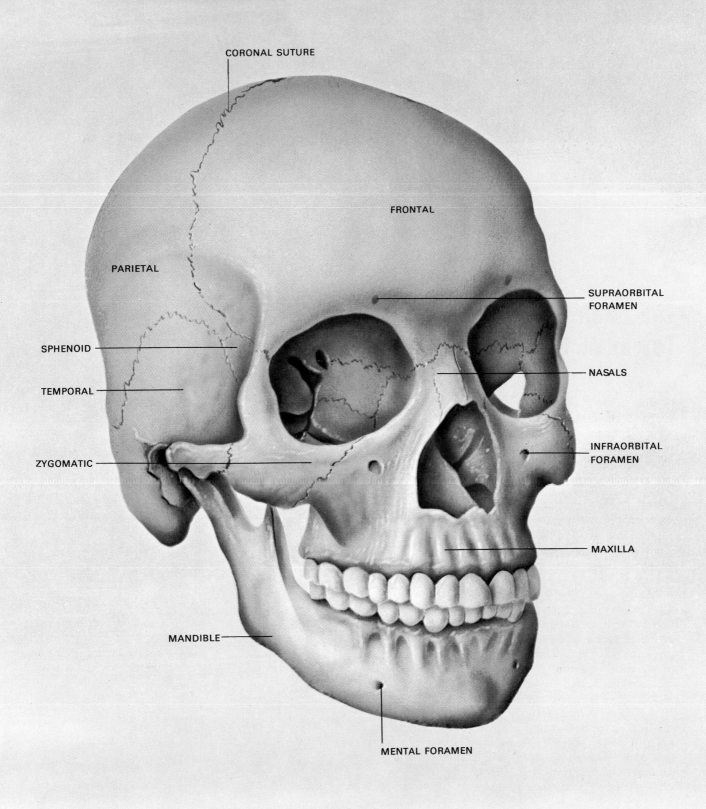

CORONAL SUTURE

FRONTAL

PARIETAL

SUPRAORBITAL
FORAMEN

SPHENOID

NASALS

TEMPORAL

INFRAORBITAL
FORAMEN

ZYGOMATIC

MAXILLA

MANDIBLE

MENTAL FORAMEN

The Skeleton: Tower of Strength

Man's skeleton was shaped by his decision more than a million years ago to stand erect. The skeleton is a tower of bones put together with hinges and joints, so superbly rigged and balanced that he can run, jump and bend despite his small feet. The adult's 206 bones anchor his muscles and shield his vital organs with a great variety of structural shapes—from the flat plates of the skull to the hollow rings of the backbone. Strong yet pliant, they have adapted with varying degrees of success to man's unique posture. The skeleton of no other creature has such long legs relative to the arms, a foot with so high an arch, and such remarkable hands—freed to become tool-making instruments with opposing thumbs once they no longer had to be used for running on or grasping tree branches. His backbone is less perfectly adapted. Human infants are born with straight spines, but after learning to walk they acquire another unique skeletal characteristic—the swayback—the price of an upright stance.

BONY SHOCK ABSORBERS

Although bones can break, they are so strong that man can engage in unnatural feats like pole-vaulting without shattering into shards. The tubular thigh bones of the athlete at right may take up to 20,000 pounds of pressure per square inch when he lands from his vault.

STERNUM

PATELLA

PARIETAL

OCCIPITAL

ULNA

RADIUS

CLAVICLE

METACARPUS

HUMERUS

CARPUS

SCAPULA

RIBS

VERTEBRAL COLUMN

HIPBONE

SACRUM

COCCYX

FEMUR

TIBIA

FIBULA

TARSUS

METATARSUS

PHALANGES

Muscles:
The Power of Pull

The body's 600-odd muscles are the cables whose pull on bones makes motion possible. Their sole function is contraction. By working in pairs, however—one muscle contracting to pull a bone forward, the other to pull it back—the muscular system is capable of an immense variety of movements, from tripping the tongue in speech to running a race.

The action of muscle on bone is most apparent in the bending of arms and legs, whose solid shafts of bone are pulled into motion by the contraction of muscles surrounding them. Other, less movable, bones are also tugged; for example, muscles of the upper torso move the bones of the rib cage during breathing by contracting and relaxing. Muscles also pull on skin or other muscles, as in a smile, a frown, and the rise and fall of the diaphragm. All these contractions are controlled and coordinated by the brain. So interrelated are muscles that one contraction usually involves many others. The racer, exercising many muscles, even grins as he runs.

MUSCLES ON THE RUN
The racers on the beach at right run by rhythmically contracting alternate teams of muscles. Muscles pictured in red are called flexors; their contractions bend hinge joints such as the knees. Muscles shown in gray are called extensors; their contractions straighten the knees again.

FRONTALIS

TRAPEZIUS

STEROCLEIDOMASTOID

DELTOID

PECTORALIS MAJOR

TRICEPS BRACHII

BICEPS BRACHII

LATISSIMUS DORSI

BRACHIORADIALIS

EXTERNAL OBLIQUE

RECTUS ABDOMINIS

RECTUS FEMORIS

GLUTEUS MAXIMUS

ILIOTIBIAL BAND

VASTUS LATERALIS

SEMIMEMBRANOSUS

GASTROCNEMIUS

BICEPS FEMORIS

SARTORIUS

SOLEUS

VASTUS MEDIALIS

ACHILLES TENDON

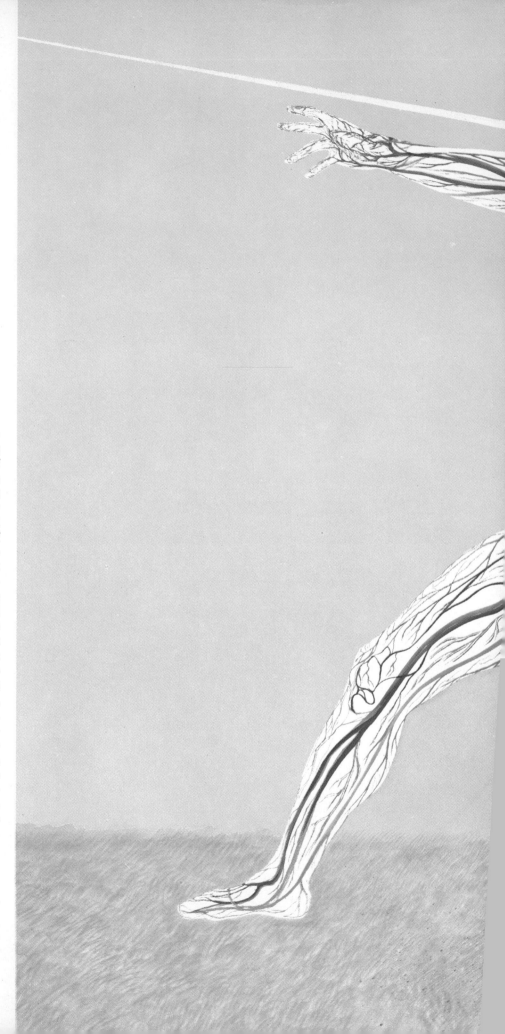

The Circulation:
One-way Network

The network pictured at right comprises some 60,000 miles of tubing which carries blood to every part of the body. Its most impressive feature is the circular manner in which it keeps the blood moving, always away from the heart in the arteries, toward the heart in the veins—in spite of gravity and in spite of millions of alternate routes. The pump of the heart gives the flow its force, sending freshly oxygenated blood surging out the aorta, the body's largest artery, and into subsidiary arteries, even to the top of the head. The arteries branch out into smaller arterioles, which in turn branch out into millions of microscopic capillaries. These capillaries eventually unite to form venules, which unite into veins, thin-walled vessels with interior valves which prevent the blood from slipping backward. Thus the spent blood streams back to the heart. A side trip to the lungs via a pulmonary network refreshes it with oxygen, and it returns to the heart ready to start anew. The entire cycle takes less than a minute.

SUPPLY ON DEMAND
The arteries *(red)* and veins *(blue)* of muscles doing energy-consuming work, such as javelin-throwing, may receive up to nine times more blood than when at rest. Muscles in arterial walls, on signals from the nervous system, can contract so that the flow goes where needed.

AXILLARY VEIN

SUBCLAVIAN VEIN

INTERNAL JUGULAR VEIN

COMMON CAROTID ARTERY

SUPERIOR VENA CAVA

SUBCLAVIAN ARTERY

AXILLARY ARTERY

AORTIC ARCH

HEART

AORTA

INFERIOR VENA CAVA

RENAL ARTERY

RENAL VEIN

COMMON ILIAC VEIN

COMMON ILIAC ARTERY

FEMORAL ARTERY

FEMORAL VEIN

Nervous System:
Sorter of Signals

The intricate task of receiving and reacting to the storm of stimuli that assault the human body is charged to the nervous system. Made up of the brain, the spinal cord and a complex network of nerves, the nervous system coordinates all the body's activities, in response to signals from both inside and outside the body. The brain is the system's headquarters. From it stem cranial nerves and the spinal cord, a cylinder of nerve tissue that runs through the backbone for 18 inches. Nerves branch out from it on either side, to embrace the body from head to toe. Some nerves are sensory nerves, carrying stimuli to the cord and brain. Others are motor nerves, along which the brain sends its orders. We react to some stimuli consciously, as when we swat a fly. Other activities—like those of the viscera—are outside our conscious control. But the three-pound brain coordinates its huge traffic of messages so well that an electron-tube computer designed to perform as well would occupy a space as big as a skyscraper.

THE PATH OF NEURAL MESSAGES
The nerve impulse that trips this athlete moves at a speed of nearly 350 feet per second—considerably faster than the discus he throws. From the brain the signal flashes through the spinal cord to a motor nerve. From there, with a chemical boost, it jumps to trigger a muscle.

50

CEREBRUM

CEREBELLUM

8 CERVICAL
NERVES

BRACHIAL PLEXUS

12
THORACIC
NERVES

RADIAL NERVE

MEDIAN NERVE

ULNAR NERVE

END OF
SPINAL CORD

CAUDA EQUINA

5 LUMBAR
NERVES

LUMBOSACRAL PLEXUS

5 SACRAL
NERVES

FEMORAL NERVE

SCIATIC NERVE

The Viscera: Fueling the Body

Although they are often called by a single name, the viscera, the neatly packed organs that fill the body's chest and abdominal cavities belong to several different systems—respiratory, digestive and urinary—which together provide the body with food and oxygen and remove wastes.

The trachea and lungs are parts of the respiratory system, which delivers oxygen to the blood. The lungs consist of millions of elastic membranous sacs which together can hold about as much air as a basketball.

The organs of the digestive system—most prominently the stomach, the large and small intestines and the liver—modify foods which the body takes in. The soft, reddish-brown liver, the largest gland in the body, literally plays hundreds of roles, from producing proteins to secreting bile.

The bladder is part of the urinary system, which regulates the body's water supply. The kidneys, located behind the stomach and liver, filter out wastes and pass them along to the bladder for storage and disposal.

VERSATILE SACS AND TUBES
If a living chest and abdominal flap were peeled back, the viscera in action would only approximate those pictured here. The lungs, for example, are constantly inflating and emptying; the 10-inch-long stomach can shrink to a flattened sac or expand to hold two quarts of food.

TRACHEA

LUNGS

HEART

LIVER

GALL BLADDER
SPLEEN
STOMACH

LARGE INTESTINE

SMALL INTESTINE

BLADDER

3

The Team of Bone and Muscle

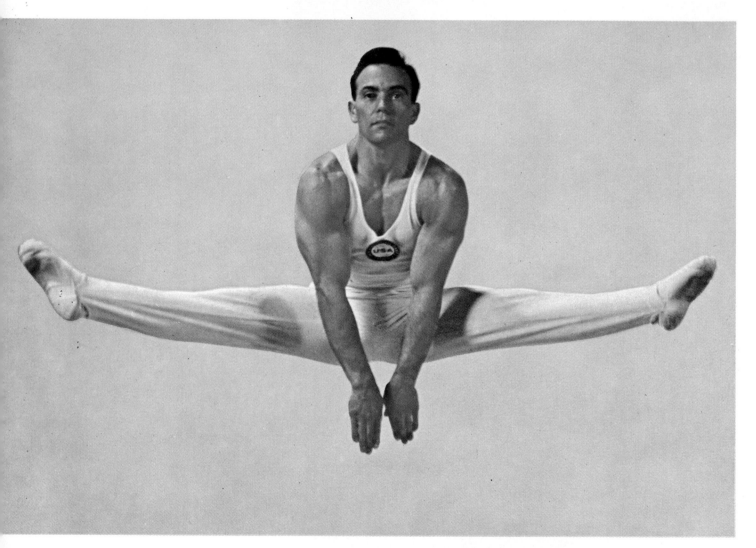

A CASE OF COORDINATION
In order to accomplish this deceptively simple-looking straddle jump, U.S. Olympics gymnast star Abie Grossfeld springs high into the air in a superb display of the workings of the body's musculoskeletal system. Even in nonathletes the daily pounding to which bones and muscles are subjected is so great that it would cause some machines to wear out after only a few years.

ONE NEW YEAR'S EVE a few years ago a small sports car skidded on an icy curve in Snoqualmie Pass in the Cascades and plunged through a guardrail down a rocky slope into the creek bed below. The driver died instantly. His 23-year-old companion was still breathing when rescuers arrived, but she looked—as one of them put it—as if every bone in her body were broken.

X-rays bore out that amateur diagnosis to an alarming extent. They showed eight ribs smashed on one side of the chest, three on the other. The left shoulder was dislocated. Several separate fracture lines criss-crossed the pelvis. The left thigh bone had snapped in the middle. No X-rays were needed to reveal the damage to the left leg; both its bones protruded in a dirty open break. "She may live," the hospital surgeon said, "but only in a wheelchair."

A little more than two years later his patient was off crutches and set to embark upon a normal life of marriage and childbearing. Skilled surgical techniques and drugs had vitally contributed to her comeback. But two other forces also played a powerful part: the extraordinary capacity of bone to mend itself, and the natural tendency of torn muscle to heal back into usefulness.

With its built-in ability for self-repair, the human framework represents a triumph of design and engineering that puts any bridge or skyscraper to shame. It has its flaws, to be sure. An S-shaped spine, for example, burdens us with aching backs and other ills—a result of man's decision to stop moving about on all fours and rear up on his hindquarters. But offsetting any structural imperfection is a functional skill responsive both to crisis and to the demands of everyday life.

The three basic elements of the musculoskeletal system—bone, muscle and connective tissue—normally perform with perfect teamwork. Their mission is to support the body, shield its delicate internal organs and make it mobile. No task force was ever more meticulously equipped and organized:

• Support for the body is supplied by the bones. Individually strong as iron girders, they are, in addition, linked by ligaments—bands of elastic, fibrous tissue—and fitted together, end to end, in joints.

• Protection for the internal organs is provided, in concert, by the bones, joints and connective tissue. Where bone movement would be dangerous, as in the pelvis or skull, the joints are rigid—glued together or even interlocked. Where movement is essential, as in the hips or shoulders, the joints are flexible—lined with cartilage, a glassy-smooth tissue which resists friction, and lubricated by synovial fluid, a secretion of egg-white consistency which acts as a "joint oil."

• Mobility for the body is supplied by the skeletal muscles. These are separate and distinct from the muscles of the internal organs, such as the visceral muscles of the stomach and intestine, and from the special cardiac muscles of the heart. The internal muscles have no relation to the bony skeleton, and operate without our conscious control. In contrast, the skeletal muscles are voluntary—subject to command. Most are attached to bone by tendons, bands of tissue less elastic and generally thicker than ligaments. Usually these muscles are paired. While one muscle "stands," relaxed, its partner tugs at the bone, much like ropes pulling at a lever. It is this mechanism which puts the body in motion.

A kick and a teeter

Supported by bone and activated by muscle, the body enjoys an incredibly wide range of movement, as forceful as sledge-hammering, as gentle as blinking. The same hand that pats a puppy pounds a desk. The same foot that teeters on tiptoe kicks a field goal. The limits of mobility are broad and the limitations relatively few; we cannot, for example, touch left forefinger to left elbow, or turn the head to look directly behind us. Even so, by stretching ligaments and muscles to make his joints unusually limber, a yogi can tie himself into a mariner's knot, wrap his feet around his neck, twist his spine and otherwise contort himself. Impersonating a pretzel is a pastime limited in its popularity, but at least it demonstrates the body's unexpected capabilities.

The grand plan of the musculoskeletal structure is all the more impressive because of the sheer number of its parts. A mature body contains more than 600 muscles and 206 bones, not counting the tiny sesamoid bones—like sesame seeds—embedded in the tendons of the thumb, big toe and other pressure points. For the bones, in fact, the figure represents a comedown; newborn babes may have more than 300. By adulthood many of these bones have fused. Not infrequently, however, fusion fails. An otherwise average person may find himself with an extra bone in the arch of the foot, and one in every 20 people has an extra rib. This appendage appears three times as often in men as in women—possibly a form of compensation for the rib Adam yielded up to Eve.

Except for these minor anomalies, the arrangement of the bones is as precise, orderly and purposeful as the parent skeletal system itself, and their distribution from top to bottom is a strikingly equable one. The skull, at the apex of the bony structure, has 29 bones. The spine, to which are attached the shoulder girdle, rib cage and hip girdle, has 26 vertebrae. The ribs number 24. The two girdles, so named because of their formation, mark the upper and lower limits of the body's trunk, or central area. From them, respectively, stem the bones of the upper and lower limbs—each with 30 bones apiece. Of the 60 bones in the two upper limbs, all but six are concentrated in the hands and wrists; of the 60 bones in the two lower limbs, all but eight are concentrated in the

GETTING THE INSIDE PICTURE

How the X-ray machine, that valuable diagnostic tool, works is diagramed below. A current heats a cathode, which ejects a stream of electrons. The electrons hit a target on the face of the anode, exciting it and producing X-rays, some of which rebound and pass through the patient. Some tissues, such as bone, block more rays than other tissues. Film behind the screen is exposed to the X-rays, producing a picture of the inner man.

POWER CONNECTION

CATHODE
X-RAY TUBE
ELECTRON STREAM
TARGET
X-RAYS
ANODE
SCREEN

ankles and feet. Thus, appropriately, more than half of all the bones in the body support those parts of it which maintain the busiest daily work schedule—our extremities.

Bones are generally classified into four types according to shape: long, short, flat or irregular. They range in size from the all-powerful thigh bone, or femur—about 20 inches long, more than an inch across at mid-shaft—to the pisiform, the smallest of the wrist bones, shaped like a split pea; this bone lies at the base of the little finger, familiarly known as the pinkie. But whatever their size or shape, almost every bone in the body is designed to fit a particular need. The most notable exception is the coccyx, man's vestigial tail.

The femur, for example, must withstand great weight and pressure. Its shaft is shaped like a hollow cylinder—an excellent design, as any engineer knows, for maximum strength with a minimum of material. Thus constructed, the thigh bone can take enormous pressures, depending upon the weight of the person and the activity at the moment. In a 125-pound woman who is simply taking a walk, for example, some points of the femur withstand a pressure of 1,200 pounds per square inch. If by some whim, she were suddenly to start jumping, this bone would be equally capable of resisting the far greater stresses involved.

Another superb example of functionalism appears in a typical vertebra of the spinal column. To help bear the weight of the body, it is formed like a solid cylinder. At the back of the cylinder, a bony ring permits passage of the spinal nerve cord, and also serves to protect it. At the back of the ring are three sharp projections, or spurs, which join with the ribs and anchor the muscles of the back.

Safe conduct in the skull

The bones which guard the various vital internal organs are also especially adapted to their assignments. The skull, the pelvis and the rib cage all provide noteworthy examples. In the skull, the bones which encase the brain are—in contrast to the wafer-thin bones of the face—thick plates, interlocked at the edges. They actually fuse when the brain reaches its mature growth. In both the male and female pelvis, the bones, while not interlocked, are tightly bound by cartilaginous joints; but in the female, during the last stage of pregnancy, these joints loosen and separate slightly to make childbirth easier. In the rib cage, which is designed to defend the heart, lungs, liver and spleen against damage, the ribs curve out from the upper vertebrae, in barrel-stave fashion, to provide a packing-crate type of protection.

The rib cage, or thorax, also provides an excellent example of another marvel of the skeletal structure: the versatility of the joints. While rigidly protecting its precious cargo, the thorax must be able to expand and

PUTTING THE PIECES BACK TOGETHER AGAIN

THE EARLY BONESETTERS
Wars and a growing efficiency in weapons created an increased demand for bonesetting devices, such as the 16th Century German leg splint *(above)* and arm stretcher *(below)*. The Greeks knew about splints, starched bandages and clay casts, and in the Fifth Century B.C., Hippocrates was treating fractures with sound techniques. In the 14th Century weights and pulleys came into use as devices for keeping broken limbs in traction.

57

A FOOTBALL FRACTURE
Different sports impose different strains on the human frame and cause different kinds of bone breaks. The fractures shown here are common. The break above occurs when the defensive player's wrist is bent backward by the ballcarrier's momentum. His wrist will be immobilized for six to eight weeks; it should heal in eight to 12 weeks.

A BROKEN LEG FOR A SKIER
This skier has just plowed into a sitzmark (literally, a "sit-mark") left by another skier. His feet are stopped in their tracks; the rest of his body continues its downhill plunge, and the resulting strain breaks the two bones of his lower leg. The fracture will normally take from four to six months before it is completely healed.

contract to permit the lungs to inflate and deflate with each breath. In front, the ribs are joined firmly to the breastbone by cartilage, but in back they are furnished with tiny gliding, rotating joints which enable them to articulate individually with the vertebrae. In contrast to these minuscule joints is the great ball-and-socket joint of the hip, which holds the rounded ball end of the femur in a fistlike grasp. Perhaps the finest proof of this joint's range of flexibility is the right-angle stance of the ballerina or of the baseball pitcher at windup.

Other joints, however, may limit motion to very specific planes (in some people the limits extend a bit more than usual, an attribute inaccurately described as double-jointedness). The knee can move only as a simple hinge. The shoulder, which can easily be dislocated if the arm rotates too widely, has a far shallower ball-and-socket joint than the hip. The head enjoys a smooth rotary motion, thanks to the two uppermost vertebrae in the neck, the atlas, named for the Greek god who carried the world on his shoulders, and the axis, which serves as a pivot for both head and atlas. It is the collaborative movement of these bones that produces two of mankind's most overworked gestures—a negative shake of the head and an affirmative nod.

However diverse in action, all bone is amazingly strong and at the same time amazingly light. In a 160-pound man only about 29 pounds represent bone weight. Steel bars of comparable size would weigh at least four or five times as much. The lightness of bone is due in part to its porosity, in part to the hollow-tube construction of the long bones of the limbs. The strength is due to bone's composition. About half its weight is made up of inorganic compounds of calcium, phosphorus and other minerals; about a quarter is made up of organic matter—a type of protein fiber called collagen, from the Greek *kolla*, glue, and *gène*, forming; almost all the remaining quarter of bone weight is, surprisingly, water. The minerals and collagen are cemented together to give bone the strength of reinforced concrete.

A bone to pick with Shakespeare

Bone's mineral content also accounts for its most notable characteristic—its hardness. The shafts of long bones are virtually as hard as granite; even in the spongy, rounded bone ends, which are relatively softer, the shape is retained long after the body itself is dead. Bone is thus the body's most enduring monument. Shakespeare was only partly right when he made his celebrated observation that the good men do is oft interred with their bones; a lot more is buried with it.

So durable is bone, in fact, that it provides our major clues to humanity's past. Skeletal remains many centuries old have helped scientists deduce the size and shape of ancient peoples, the kind of work they did, and the arthritis and other ailments they suffered. There is even evidence that beings with human features existed not merely a million years ago, as once believed, but 10 million. In 1958 an almost complete skeleton was discovered embedded in a block of coal in the roof of a Tuscan mine in central Italy. Fossil pieces found earlier in the area had been thought to belong to some apelike creature, formally titled *Oreopithecus* but inevitably, because of the locale, dubbed "The Abominable Coalman." Scrutiny of the bones by a Swiss paleontologist, Dr. Johannes Hurzeler, showed, however, that *Oreopithecus* was more manlike than apelike. The keys to the puzzle proved to be the skeleton's pelvis, spine and chin bones—all readily identifiable despite their protracted interment.

Skeletons and time clocks

The sex, approximate age, race and medical history of a person long deceased are among other data preserved by bone. The telltale marks are many. Dr. Wilton M. Krogman, professor of physical anthropology at the University of Pennsylvania, and long renowned among police and insurance men for his skill as a bone detective, has, for example, determined the sex of a murder victim by the size of ridges above the eyes and at the back of the skull. He has been able to judge age, give or take a few years, by ascertaining whether the long bones and wisdom teeth were fully grown and whether the seams of the skull bones were fully fused; at the age of 40, for example, they are about three-quarters fused. Another technique he has employed as a clue to age is to X-ray decalcified areas in the shoulder blades. Here, as elsewhere in the body, the loss of calcium irreversibly increases with the years. "From birth to death," Dr. Krogman notes, "the skeleton punches a time clock."

Throughout this inexorable process, however, bone continues its basic job of supporting the body and providing the joint articulations required for smooth, effortless movement. It performs so inconspicuously that only some malfunction will remind us of its presence. The joints may become inflamed and swollen, resulting in the painful, crippling condition which we know as arthritis. Simple wear and tear on the cartilage of the weight-bearing joints in particular may cause the form of arthritis which we call "old folks' rheumatism." A part of one of the "disks" of the spinal column—thick pads of cartilage which separate the vertebrae—may protrude and press agonizingly against a nerve. Or the fibrous tissue and tendon supporting the knee, ankle or wrist bones may stretch or tear, resulting in sprain.

Fractures, a classic affliction of the human race, occur so commonly that few people escape them. The very fact that bone is brittle makes it vulnerable to a break, especially through a blow or fall. Because men since time immemorial have tried to stop a fall with outstretched hands,

A TOUGH BREAK FOR A TUMBLER
This trampoline artist has fractured his lateral malleolus—his ankle. In gymnastics even the slightest error in timing can exert a powerful force on a susceptible bone at an awkward angle and cause a painful fracture. This man's ankle will be immobilized in a cast for eight weeks; it should heal completely in 12.

the commonest fracture is a tipped-back break of the wrist, called a Colles fracture after the 19th Century Irish surgeon, Abraham Colles, who wrote the first comprehensive description of its forklike deformity.

Happily bone, while susceptible to breakage, is also susceptible to solid mending, largely through its own efforts. The self-healing begins, in fact, at the moment of fracture, and in an orderly sequence of events. First, broken blood vessels at the fracture site form an enveloping blood clot, or hematoma. In a few days minerals from the sharp ends of the broken bone have been reabsorbed into the bloodstream, leaving the ends soft and rubbery. At the same time a fibrous lacing of connective tissue has grown through the hematoma, holding the fracture fragments together with a weak cellular glue. Within this sticky substance a special kind of cell, the osteoblast (literally, "bone-maker"), appears to strengthen the bone ends, depositing insoluble calcium phosphate and other minerals. In another two or three weeks soft, calcium-rich new bone, or callus, can be seen on X-rays, bridging the gap between the bone ends. When the callus hardens, the mended bone is ready to resume its job of weight-bearing and support. Often the healing is so complete that eventually the fracture site cannot be detected even by X-ray.

The process, however, takes time. Compared to torn skin, which may repair itself in days, or injured muscle, which may be ready for work again within weeks, bone may require months to heal. The deposit of enough calcium to strengthen and harden new bone is gradual. Bone cells grow and reproduce slowly. Blood supply to bone is relatively poor; as a result, when bone becomes infected its resistance is relatively low. All these problems are compounded, as in the case of the Snoqualmie Pass accident victim mentioned earlier, when a bone is broken into many pieces, or crushed out of shape, or severely displaced.

The orthopedic witch doctor

Before such bone can begin to heal, the fragments must first be returned to their proper anatomical positions, either by manipulation or surgery, and must be immobilized there by means of plaster casts, metal plates, pins, nails or screws. Despite these relative advances in medical technology, however, the basic technique of bone-setting has not radically changed over the centuries. In his treatise entitled "On Fractures," Hippocrates was passing along a skill already ancient when he advised his readers exactly how to manipulate a broken arm to position the bones correctly before splinting, so as to ensure their return to their "natural direction." Venerable if crude techniques still turn the trick today. The dislodged or fractured bones of many an African tribesman have been reset by witch doctors with an orthopedic flair, using forked sticks for crutches and caked mud, instead of plaster, for casts.

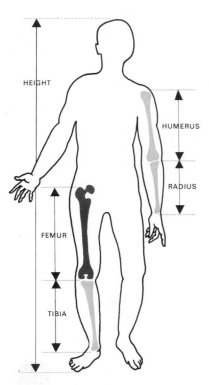

HEIGHT AND BONES

So precise is the relationship between various bones and height that anthropological detectives, with one dried bone as a clue, can closely estimate its owner's former living height. For example, if a 17.9-inch femur is found, the arithmetic table at right gives a living stature of five and a half feet. Interestingly, a radius long in proportion to the other three bones (as in apes) indicates a relatively short person.

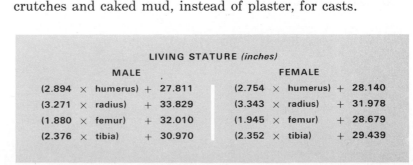

LIVING STATURE (inches)			
MALE		FEMALE	
(2.894 × humerus) +	27.811	(2.754 × humerus) +	28.140
(3.271 × radius) +	33.829	(3.343 × radius) +	31.978
(1.880 × femur) +	32.010	(1.945 × femur) +	28.679
(2.376 × tibia) +	30.970	(2.352 × tibia) +	29.439

By contrast with the ills that bone is prey to, its partner in the skeletal system—muscle—is, because of its exceptionally rich blood supply, the most infection-free of all the body's basic tissues. The muscular troubles most people are likely to encounter are of an everyday sort induced by strain or overuse. One of the commonest ailments is chronic myalgia, the muscle tension associated both with fatigue and with a state of undue alertness. Another is the soreness which afflicts us the day after we have overtaxed some portion of the anatomy beyond its ordinary exertions; in the dignified language of the doctor, this is known as benign overuse myalgia. The athletes among us occasionally suffer a bruised leg or thigh muscle as a result of a blow or forceful stretch; this is the condition which laymen label Charley horse, after the lame old nag who hauled the family surrey in the days before internal combustion.

A muscle for Mona Lisa

Like the bones, the skeletal muscles range in size and shape to suit the particular functions they perform. The muscles of the face, permitting a raised eyebrow, a frown or the faint smile of a Mona Lisa, are, some of them, less than an inch long; so are the muscles which unleash a lifetime of tongue-wagging. At the floor of the chest is the dome-shaped diaphragm, which is the main muscle involved in breathing, and is also involved in coughing, sneezing, laughing and sighing. In the neck and back, long, straplike muscles hold the head upright. The bulging, triangular deltoids of the shoulders raise the arms. The biceps and triceps of the upper arms bend—and unbend—the elbows. The broad pectoralis major muscles, those rippling signs of the he-man, move the arms across the chest. The massive gluteal muscles of the buttocks help us stand up and walk. The longest muscle in the body is in the thigh; it is known as sartorius, from the Latin for tailor, because it comes into play in the cross-legged position which tailors traditionally assumed. Sartorius and four bundles of muscles on each side of it called the quadriceps not only move the legs but also help us maintain our balance.

Whether large or small, the skeletal muscles can perform with prodigious speed and power. Such qualities can be literally of life-or-death importance, enabling the body to move in response to sudden and drastic changes in the external environment. Skeletal muscle can get into action within a few hundredths of a second, exert an enormous concentrated pull on the bone to which it is attached and, when necessary, support 1,000 times its own weight.

All muscle, visceral and cardiac as well as skeletal, moves by contracting itself—a unique characteristic which distinguishes it from any other body tissue. In the case of skeletal muscle, the individual cells, ordinarily long and thin, become shorter and fatter under stimulus and take on their tremendous pulling power. Once the stimulus has passed, the muscle relaxes, settling back into its original shape.

The precise nature of the process of contraction and relaxation—an extremely complex one both electrochemical and mechanical in nature—is still the subject of intensive research. It is known that a skeletal muscle contracts at the brain's command, responding to signals sent along nerves which are linked to muscle fibers. These signals spark a series of chemical changes in the muscle, which results in the conversion of chemical into mechanical energy, thus producing the actual movement of muscle contraction.

The strategy of two combs

A great deal more has been learned about the mechanical part of the process than about the chemical part. When the brain signals arrive at the junction of nerve and muscle, they penetrate deep into the tiny fibrils which compose muscle fiber. Each fibril, in turn, consists of rows of minute, filament-like protein molecules of two types, called actin and myosin. These face each other like two combs with their teeth partially interlocked. The muscle contraction takes place when the actin and myosin filaments glide toward each other as if to mesh. This action shortens the fibril, hence the muscle fiber, hence the muscle itself.

The chemical changes which bring the mechanics into play are as yet by no means fully understood. It is generally believed that one important such change occurs when the brain signals reach the nerve-muscle junction, which is located on the membrane of the muscle cell; a substance called acetylcholine, which acts as an excitant, is released, thus putting the muscle membrane on alert. The actual energy which the muscle needs in order to contract is thought to be supplied by the breakdown of a substance known as ATP (for adenosine triphosphate). This breakdown, in turn, is made possible by the conversion of glycogen, the powerful fuel which the body supplies to muscle in the form of glucose, a sugar. The muscle contraction itself is touched off by the release of calcium from the muscle membrane. The calcium, according to recent research, may also play a part in muscle relaxation; once released, it is stored in between the tiny muscle fibrils, in a granular network which goes by the jawbreaking technical name, sarcoplasmic reticulum. When a certain amount of it has been stored, relaxation follows.

If it is taxed repeatedly, without rest, muscle tires and ultimately stops contracting altogether. How long it can stay the course without faltering also depends, of course, on its basic health. The work a muscle does, or can do, is directly related to its size and its blood supply. Doctors who prescribe a daily dozen for their flabby patients are no Torquemadas in modern guise; exercise is vital if muscle tissue is to remain in

TENDON

BONE

MUSCLE

LIGAMENT

TEAMWORK IN THE LIMBS

Bone, muscle, tendon and ligament work together in an intimate relationship to move the body. Here, in the human arm and shoulder, bones give the limb its tensile strength and its basic framework, and are also busy centers for the manufacture of red blood cells. The limb is moved by skeletal muscles, which may be attached directly to the bone, or by tough connecting tendons. Ligaments prevent the bones from slipping apart at the joints.

good condition. Unless used, muscles tend to shrink and waste away.

In so doing, they deprive the body not only of its mobility but also of an important source of its heat. Few people realize that skeletal muscle helps keep them snugly warm, indeed sometimes too much so for comfort. Of the energy released by glycogen, one of the body's fuels, only a quarter is used for muscular movement; fully three fourths burns off as heat. The more strenuous the activity, as in running, dancing or pushing the furniture around, the warmer we feel.

The great team of muscle and bone—aided by the connective tissue that holds them and other parts of the body together—has provided man, ever since he became man, with an unbeatable combination. We do not, by any means, know all there is to know about muscle and bone, and research continues into their makeup and behavior. Related to the studies of muscle contraction mentioned earlier, experiments have been performed in which the nerve ends connected to slow and fast muscle fibers are switched. Both types of fiber react to a brain signal with tremendous speed, but the slow fibers comparatively less so. Switching their nerve ends, it has been found, reverses the speed. Thus a whole new vista for exploration has opened up concerning the possible influence of specific types of nerve on muscle.

In the bone field, medical scientists have been evaluating the inorganic part of bone—the solid crystalline structure of the bone minerals. These crystals tend to absorb both beneficial substances, such as fluorine, and harmful substances, such as radium or radioactive strontium from nuclear fallout, which belong to the same chemical family as calcium and can be absorbed in its stead. Research has shown, however, that eventually the crystals reach a point of satiety. Conceivably, some time in the future, a way may be found to control what they absorb, and in what quantities.

Rescue of a sleepwalker

Through ever-improving surgical techniques, the replacement of both bone and muscle, when hopelessly injured or diseased, has met with increasing success. Both muscle and tendon can be transplanted in certain cases. In recent years a college shot-put star lost the biceps in his right arm when he thrust his arm through a window while sleepwalking; a part of one of his leg muscles was split and effectively transplanted to substitute for the ruined arm muscle. The grafting of bone—whether from the patient's own body, from the deep-freeze human bone banks now common in most major U.S. cities, or from animal (usually cow) bone —is no longer news. One recent advance, however, is significant. The human body is inclined to reject animal bones because they contain certain substances which it cannot tolerate. Improved processing has made

MOTOR FIBERS

SENSORY FIBER
SENSORY FIBER
MOTOR FIBER

ARTERY

THE NERVE-MUSCLE PARTNERSHIP
This highly simplified illustration shows a muscle and some of the nerve fibers that service it. Motor neurons—nerves that carry orders from the brain—branch out their fibers when they reach a muscle, and a neuron may control as many as 150 muscle fibers. Sensory neurons feed back information to the brain to be evaluated. The motor nerve fiber to the artery stimulates contraction of that vessel's muscular wall, thus controlling the blood flow.

it possible to remove such substances without weakening the physical structure of these bones. Increasingly they have been grafted onto human bone with virtually no struggle against them by the body's immunological forces.

In other notable areas of bone disability, neither animal nor human bone grafts have proved as satisfactory as out-and-out mechanical replacements. Knuckle joints crippled by arthritis are now supplanted by stainless steel or Vitallium. Metal hinges—and specially molded rods —can often be used as permanent substitutes for hip, elbow and knee joints. The success of such operations stems from the body's toleration of inert material.

For all the problems these developments imply, the remarkable fact about bone and muscle is how little trouble they give us. Almost every waking moment we subject them to a formidable amount of pounding and abuse. The average person walks some 19,000 steps a day—about eight miles. His muscles do an amount of daily work equivalent to lifting dozens of tons of wheat onto a wagon four feet high. Some machines, after only a few years of such treatment, would certainly become obsolescent. The body stands up to it for some three-score-and-ten years and still—at least insofar as its bone and muscle are concerned—may be little the worse for wear.

Triumphs of Structure and Design

Bone is the structural steel and the reinforced concrete of the human body. It supports the body the way a steel framework supports a skyscraper, and it protects its vital organs the way a cast-concrete roof protects a building's occupants. In filling these structural assignments, the human body solves problems of design and construction familiar to the architect and engineer. Among them are how to support a tower that cannot stand by itself, and how to build a protective covering that combines strength and lightness. To achieve its results, architecture uses a wide variety of materials—steel, aluminum, concrete; the skeleton uses bone only, but bone fashioned into a wide range of shape and size for a wide range of uses. Yet, the solutions are notably similar. It is not that architecture copied nature (much less the converse) but that, for given problems, the best solutions—in engineering as in the human frame—often are similar.

A SWINGING JOINT

Great demands are made upon the joint between the hip and the thigh: it must firmly support the weight of the upper body while standing, yet be flexible enough to allow leg mobility in many planes while moving. The effective solution is a ball-and-socket joint *(opposite)*. When similar flexibility is required, the same joint is used in mechanical devices such as the TV "rabbit ears."

OKLAHOMA CITY TELEVISION TOWER

THE SPINE

Both structures shown on these pages would
be happier flat on the ground or floor. They
could not possibly stand by themselves.
To be upright they must be held in place by
elaborate systems of guy wires and supports.
On the opposite page is one of the tallest
man-made constructions in the world—
a TV tower in Oklahoma City. At right is
the human body's most central structural
member—the spine. The tower, 1,572 feet tall,
would instantly collapse without the web
of steel guy lines which braces it against
the elements. Similarly the spine, a collection
of 26 articulated bones, must be held together
and kept upright by muscles and ligaments.
Among these are two straps of ligament
that run up the spine, front and back, to keep
it firm, and a pair of the body's largest
muscle masses, to keep the spine from
sliding. Atop the spine rides the head;
at the bottom the column is anchored in
the pelvis. Attached to it are the ribs;
running vertically through it are the trunk lines
of the nervous system; and at its very bottom
is the vestigial tail bone, or coccyx—one of
the few useless bones in the human body.
The spine shown in this picture is seen
in right profile and, of course, without any of
its supporting muscles and ligaments.

THE SPINE

THE CRANIUM

ROME SPORTS ARENA

68

THE CRANIUM

One of the most important duties assigned to
the body's bones is to protect the brain.
The eight thin pieces of armor plate which form
the cranium, the brain's protective helmet
(opposite), meet at joints called sutures *(right)*.
In children the sutures are not fused, but they
become rigid splices when the child is grown.
The mature cranium is much like a modern
architectural form called thin-shell construction.
The building shown below, fashioned by
the Italian engineering genius Pier Nervi, is
a graceful example of this construction.
It uses a very thin layer of concrete which,
because it is curved, is self-bracing and rigid;
it is exceptionally strong for its weight—just as
an eggshell is strong and light. The roof shell
below has 1,620 small pieces; joined, they form
a unit which, like the cranium, is designed to
offer maximum protection for minimum weight.

CRANIAL SUTURES

THE ELBOW

Man's most versatile tools are his arms—highly
flexible extensions which permit him to reach
out, grasp things and manipulate them.
The arm's splendid utility is provided by a series
of joints that allow it to bend, twist and turn.
Most prominent of these is the elbow,
a smoothly operated hinge between the
carefully fitted bone endings of the upper and
lower arm. At left is a triple-exposure
photograph of the inside of the right elbow,
showing the forearm bones straight out
horizontally, bent up, and folded back toward
the shoulder. Below, a lineup of five cranes
demonstrates a man-made form of this
flexibility. These cranes, too, provide access to
out-of-the-way places—with their elbow joints.
The chief difference is that the cranes work
hydraulically, while the elbow is operated by
groups of muscles and tendons—which at the
same time make the human arm more
shapely than a mechanical cherry picker.

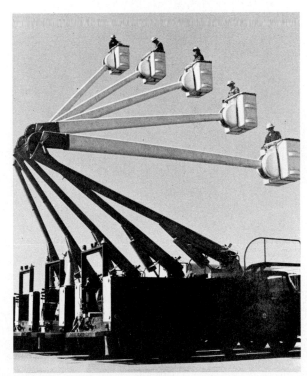

MECHANICAL ELBOWS ON CRANES

THE ELBOW IN TRIPLE EXPOSURE

MODEL OF SPACE FRAME

THE PELVIS

When a man stands, his entire weight is carried
by the bones of his legs down to his feet.
But when he sits, the weight is carried on
the two arches of bone *(opposite)* extending
below the flaring wings of the pelvis.
A seated person's weight is transferred to
the lower rims of the arches, areas known as
the ischial tuberosities. The arches are simply
and efficiently designed for taking the weight of
the torso as it is passed on by the spine.
The design is echoed in the building model
above. Here the weight of the roof is gathered
in sloping columns and carried to several
supporting points. All material unnecessary
for stress-bearing is removed and the result
is a light, open structure, called a space frame,
that provides a lot of solid support.

73

THE FEMUR

The strains placed on any supporting member, be it a floor or a bone, are never uniform. The curved beams on the underside of the floor below are placed to add strength only where the stresses occur. The cross-hatching of lines inside the bone on the opposite page does the same thing. The bone is the femur, or thigh bone, the longest and strongest in the body. The lines are ridges of bone built up in those planes where stresses occur. Should a fracture change the stresses (in the femur, they can be two tons per square inch), the living bone shifts its stress lines accordingly—a triumph of bone that buildings have never matched.

REINFORCED CONCRETE FLOOR

4

The Heart and Its Couriers

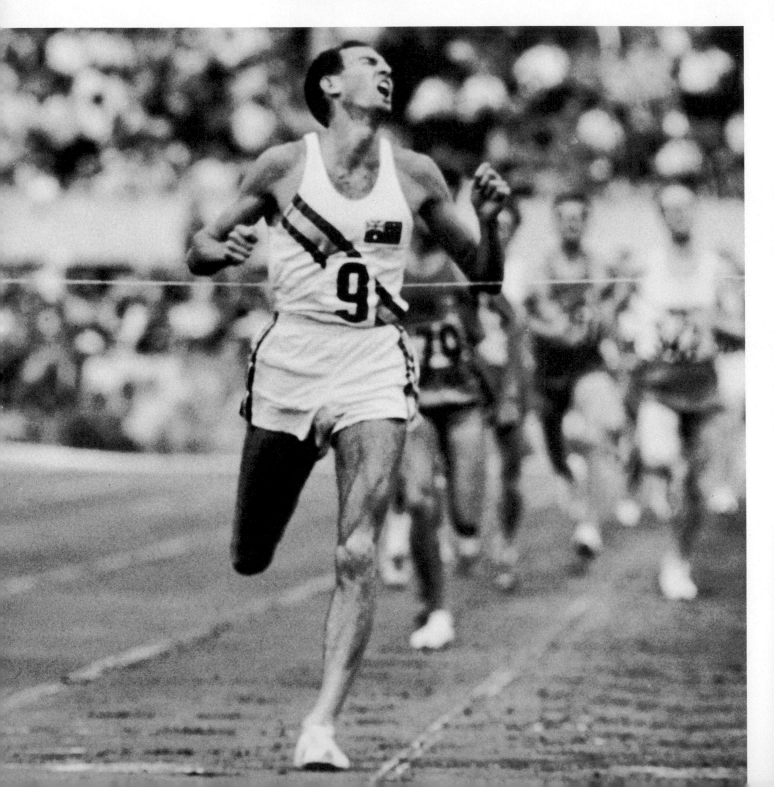

THE TEEMING TRAFFIC of the busiest metropolis presents a study in sheer inertia when compared to the ceaseless activity within our own bodies. Day and night, loading and unloading goes on at every one of the body's trillions of cells. Food and oxygen are taken on; waste products are taken off. The process slows somewhat during sleep, but it never halts. A stoppage would, indeed, signal death.

Like a great city, the body needs a transport system to carry its vital cargoes to and fro. This network—the circulatory, or cardiovascular, system—has its freeways, underpasses, cloverleafs, subsidiary roads, quiet streets and back alleys. In the nomenclature of the body, the lines of supply bear the labels of artery, arteriole, capillary, venule and vein. The total distance they cover, within the confines of the body, is conservatively estimated at 60,000 miles.

The major means of transport within this vast complex is blood. Its flow is controlled by the heart. Under impetus of the heart's pumping action, the blood, with its freight, makes continuous round trips, without pause, in and out of the heart, through the rest of the body, and back into the heart to be sent out again. The heart pumps so steadily and powerfully that in a single day it pushes the 10 pints of blood in the average adult body through more than 1,000 complete circuits, thus actually pumping 5,000 to 6,000 quarts of blood a day in all.

The realization that the same small amount of blood circulated again and again was, in fact, the key to our basic understanding of the entire circulatory system. This knowledge is comparatively recent; proof that the blood went repeated rounds, and that the system therefore had to be a closed circuit, came just three centuries ago.

Even the earliest man, of course, was aware of his heart; he could feel it beat and pound. He also sensed that the strange red fluid spurting from a fresh wound was related to life and death. As sophistication grew, the heart and blood began to be associated. One Chinese medical treatise of some 3,000 years ago actually hit on the right answer. "The heart," it reported, "regulates all the blood of the body. . . . The blood current flows continuously in a circle and never stops." Later peoples, however, failed to pick up this precious nugget. They amassed increasingly accurate data about the structure of the heart and blood vessels, and continued to guess wrong about the way the system performed.

The Egyptians, for example, knew that the vessels originated in the heart and linked it with the rest of the body. But they also believed that these channels carried various items like tears and urine along with blood. The Greeks lingered over theories that the heart was the seat of the intelligence and of an "innate heat" that generated the body's so-called four humors—black and yellow bile, phlegm and blood. The last of the Greek medical luminaries, Galen, gave no credence to the notion

THE SURGE TO VICTORY
The stout heart of Herb Elliott, the Australian track star, makes it possible for him to drive to the tape to win a 1960 Olympics race *(opposite)*. In time of strenuous physical activity, the heart puts on its most spectacular performance. It pumps at a much faster rate than usual, in response to an immediate increase in the demand for blood by muscles involved in the exertion.

CHALLENGER OF GALEN'S GOSPEL
Galen said blood flowed back and forth like a tide. But William Harvey *(above)* proved with the experiment below that blood in veins can run only one way—toward the heart.

ONE-WAY VEINS
Harvey pressed blood upward from a vein section. If he released his lower finger, blood flowed into the section. But if he lifted his upper finger, blood would not run backward.

that blood might circulate. As noted in Chapter 1, he preferred to compare the blood's movement to that of the tides. Once it flowed from the heart, Galen asserted, it ebbed back on occasion to dump its impurities, sometimes using the lungs for the same purpose. The casual picture conjured up is similar to that of a driver drifting into the first handy gas station along the turnpike to have his oil checked.

The road to immortality

Galen's pronouncements on the blood, as on other matters, were long regarded as inviolable as Holy Writ. With slight modification, they persisted until a 17th Century Englishman, William Harvey, placed the affairs of the heart in proper perspective and gained medical immortality as a result.

Research, reasoning and a bit of mathematical reckoning helped Harvey discover the mechanics of blood circulation. Bent on a physician's career, he went to study at the University of Padua. Italy was then under the spell of the great Galileo and his new principles of dynamics. All sorts of mechanical devices, including the pump and valve, were being used to advance the fledgling science of motion. By a historical fortuity, Harvey's anatomy professor, the renowned Fabricius, had just done a detailed study of the valves in the human veins; that the heart itself had valves had been learned as long ago as Greek times.

Today we know that the valves—thin, membranous folds—prevent the reflux of the blood once it goes through them, compelling it to go one way. Once past the heart valves, the blood moves along the arteries, always away from the heart; once past a venous valve, it moves farther along the veins, always toward the heart. Fabricius, faithful to Galen, missed the import of his own findings. Harvey, however, began to wonder if Galileo's theories of movement might not also apply to the flow of blood within the human interior—a notable early example of the fruitful union of science and medicine.

Back in London, Harvey pursued his quest for more than two decades. He vivisected 15 different species of animals, examining the exposed heart and the way it expanded and contracted, and studying the arrangement of blood vessels. He also experimented on living human beings, applying various pressures to those veins and arteries visible from the outside. When tightly bandaged, the veins would swell, but the arteries would not, and vice versa. Harvey thereby confirmed their separate functions as incoming and outgoing channels for the blood.

His crowning achievement was to prove that the blood circulated as a result of the heart's mechanical action. First he had to determine the volume of blood pumped by the heart. To do so he used Galileo's method for the quantitative calculation of moving objects. First he measured the capacity of the dilated heart of a cadaver. The most blood the largest section of it could hold was two ounces. Harvey figured that the heart beat 1,000 times every half hour, pushing a half ounce of blood out with each beat. As it turned out, these figures were gross underestimates, but they nevertheless proved his point. According to Harvey's reckoning, the heart had to work over 1,000 by 1/2 ounces of blood every half hour—500 ounces, or 31 pounds. This was more than twice the blood in the entire body of a husky male. Manifestly, the heart had to be pumping the same blood again and again. "I began to think," Harvey wrote, "whether there might not be a movement, as it were, in a circle." He published his theories in 1628, in the classic *De Motu Cordis et Sanguinis* ("On the Movement of the Heart and Blood"). A startled medical world found them irrefutable.

Harvey was never able to pinpoint the place where the blood ceased moving away from the heart and began moving toward it. Four years after his death in 1657 the answer was found by the Italian physiologist Marcello Malpighi. Peering at the lungs of a frog under a microscope, an instrument not available to Harvey, he discovered the connecting links between veins and arteries—the capillaries, smallest of all blood vessels, so slender that 10 of them together are no thicker than a hair.

With the work of Harvey and Malpighi, the disarray of known fact about the circulatory system could be sorted out, and the picture we have of it today began to emerge more clearly.

A shape for sentimentalists

The heart itself is no bigger than a good-sized fist. It weighs less than a pound, and its shape resembles the popular Valentine image sufficiently to satisfy the sentimentalists. It lies, pointed downward, in the chest cavity, at about the mid-center body line. The walls of the heart are of thick muscle, twisted into rings, whorls and loops. Within them are four hollow chambers: a left and a right receiving chamber, or atrium, and below them a left and a right pumping chamber, or ventricle. In the right atrium is the sinus node—a minute blob with a mammoth job. Composed of special, nervelike muscle tissue found nowhere else in the body, the sinus node starts the heartbeat and sets its pace, much like the coxswain of a racing shell.

A solid partition of muscle, the septum, separates the left and right sides of the heart. Before Harvey, a stubbornly held misconception was that the blood moved through the heart by seeping through pores in the septum. The passages, however, open not from side to side but from top to bottom. These openings—with valves to control the direction of blood flow—connect the left atrium with the left ventricle, and the right atrium with the right ventricle. In effect, the heart is thus two

BLOOD FLOW

VALVE

VALVES TO REGULATE FLOW

If veins were simply long tubes, blood would rush into a person's feet every time he stood up. The blood flow in most veins is regulated by valves. When blood flows toward the heart, the valves allow it to pass. However, if the blood starts to go the wrong way *(small arrows)*, the valves fill up and stop the backflow. Defective valves allow the pressure of an unbroken column of blood from the heart to distend blood vessels in the legs, causing varicose veins.

pumps back to back. To get from one side of the heart to the other the blood must go the long way around, through the body.

Since the blood travels endlessly, an arbitrary choice must be made of a starting point to describe its route. Assume that a batch of fresh blood has just moved into the left atrium. At this point the heart is between beats—an interval of about three fifths of a second; it is only during this relaxation that the receiving chambers fill up. Then the atrium contracts, shoving the blood down into the left ventricle. As the ventricle contracts in turn, the blood is squeezed. This forces shut the left atrioventricular valve and forces open another valve leading to the aorta, the body's main artery. Out into this surges the blood.

The ramifications of an arch

The aorta, about one inch wide, curves in a great arch—up from the heart, down along the backbone into the abdomen. From it other large arteries lead to the head, the digestive organs, the arms and the legs. From these branch the smaller arterioles, and from these the tiny capillaries, thousands of them in each of a countless number of networks—the last station on the blood's outward-bound journey.

Any fluid driven by a pump, and flowing in a circuit of closed channels, necessarily operates under pressure; the nearer to the pump, the stronger the pressure. If the aorta were opened, the blood would spout a column five to six feet high. The large arteries therefore have much tougher walls than do their branches—thick layers of muscle and elastic tissue with lots of give. The importance of this resiliency is perhaps best appreciated when the walls harden as a result of the deposit of fatty materials and calcium. This condition, with its coincident constriction of the artery channels, is known as atherosclerosis—often called arteriosclerosis. Healthy arterial walls, however, stretch and rebound with each heartbeat. This movement is what we feel as the pulse, at any area of the body where the arteries lie close to the surface.

By the time the blood reaches the capillaries it is moving at a relatively slow rate, along channels so narrow that its own cells, the corpuscles, must slither through sideways. Here the blood discharges its load of dissolved food and oxygen. These leak through the microscopically thin capillary walls, across a watery bridge provided by a fluid called lymph, and into the body's cells. Back into the bloodstream, via the same route, come carbon dioxide, urea and uric acid—castoffs from the cell. This brisk maneuver is executed in an area whose size may be judged by the fact that no capillary lies more than a hair's breadth away from a cell.

In yielding up oxygen and taking on waste, the blood turns color from bright to dull red. It now starts back to the heart, trickling from the capillaries into the venules—small veins—with which they merge. The ven-

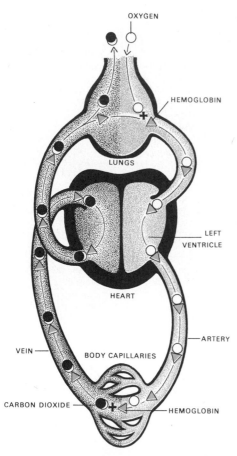

A TRANSPORT SYSTEM FOR THE BODY

The bloodstream is a vast transport system that carries oxygen to the tissues and brings carbon dioxide to the lungs to be expelled. Oxygen-laden blood is pumped from the left ventricle of the heart through the arteries and into the tiniest capillaries, where cells snatch up oxygen and turn over carbon dioxide to the red blood cells' hemoglobin. The blood flows back to the lungs, where the process begins again.

ules converge into larger veins and then into the two largest, the *venae cavae*, just above and below the heart. The blood empties into the right atrium, descends into the right ventricle, then moves out through a large artery—the pulmonary artery—leading to the lungs. The lungs supply the blood with fresh oxygen and send it, newly scarlet and reinvigorated, to the left atrium, to start its round of the body all over again.

The entire intricate, tortuous process—from first to second entry of the left atrium—takes the blood the incredibly brief time of about 20 seconds.

Moreover, the general circuit of the body—the systemic, so called—is only one of several routes which the blood tirelessly travels. Its route to and from the lungs, described above, is known as the pulmonary circulation, and is regarded as the other major circuit besides the systemic. The systemic circulation also has a number of special divisions, local but altogether essential, around which the blood simultaneously zips to aid in the function of particular vital organs. These local circulations include the renal (to the kidneys), the portal (to the liver), the cerebral (to the brain) and the coronary (to the heart itself).

A case of supply and demand

Fast as the heart pumps the blood under ordinary circumstances, the speed is markedly stepped up in response to special demand from some part of the body. A commuter dashes for a train; his leg muscles instantly require an extra surge of blood. They get it, thanks to capillaries elsewhere in the body which temporarily close because their need for blood is not so urgent. The capillaries of the stomach and intestine pass up their usual helpings of blood quite often on such occasions; on the other hand, they are likely to be more demanding than usual after a meal, when their own capacity is taxed to help in the digestive process. It is for this reason that we can be drowsy or sluggish after a meal; the blood is going to the digestive tract instead of to the brain.

During strenuous exercise, heavy physical labor or any kind of stress, the heart may pump eight times as much blood as in a period of relative relaxation—as many as 12 gallons a minute. To pump an equal amount of liquid, a hand pump considerably larger would have to work a lot longer. Yet the heart adapts to a short-term increase in work load without harm; it slows and rests when the demand falls off.

Even when the demand persists, the heart adjusts. Its muscles thicken, its chambers enlarge and it may actually double in size. The heart of a businessman with hypertension may fill half his chest cavity. In hypertension—high blood pressure—a variety of factors ranging from kidney malfunction to nervous strain may combine to create a resistance to the flow of blood through the arterioles, causing the heart to pump harder to surmount this obstacle. Whatever the cause, the heart, when forced into

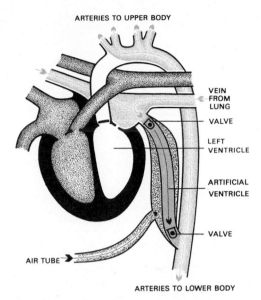

ARTERIES TO UPPER BODY

VEIN FROM LUNG

VALVE

LEFT VENTRICLE

ARTIFICIAL VENTRICLE

VALVE

AIR TUBE

ARTERIES TO LOWER BODY

A NEW PUMP FOR AILING HEARTS

The heart's most important pumping is done by the left ventricle. Now an artificial left ventricle has been developed to replace a damaged one. A double tube, the size and shape of a small banana, is inserted in the chest cavity to bypass the real ventricle. Valves, like those used in a snorkel, regulate the direction of blood flow. Air is pumped from a bedside compressor into the tube's jacket, simulating a heartbeat.

RIGHT SUBCLAVIAN VEIN

LEFT SUBCLAVIAN VEIN

RIGHT LYMPH DUCT

THORACIC DUCT

NODE

LYMPH SYSTEM IN A MAN

LYMPH VESSELS SERVING THE STOMACH

THE BLOOD'S DRAINING SYSTEM

Throughout the body there is an extensive network which carries lymph. The lymph vessels collect fluids which have seeped through the blood vessels' walls, and return them to the bloodstream via two main lymphatic ducts emptying into two subclavian veins near the heart. The lymph nodes—enlarged tissue masses in the lymph vessels—are filtering devices for removing dead cells and other foreign matter.

consistent overwork, pumps less efficiently. It tries to compensate by beating more frantically, until it cannot keep up, and fails.

A failing heart, however, can often be restored with almost miraculous dispatch by a potent chemical prepared from *Digitalis purpurea*, the common foxglove herb. The curative powers of this plant revealed themselves about 1776, through the ailing person of the principal of Brasenose College, Oxford. This gentleman suffered from dropsy—a waterlogging of the tissues in part due to heart failure—until he abandoned orthodox remedies and tried a homemade formula for dropsy, a special tea brewed by an old woman of Shropshire. The results were so astonishingly good that word spread. Analyzing the beverage, a compound of some 20 or more varieties of herb, a local doctor, William Withering, proved foxglove to be the active ingredient. Under its Latin name of *digitalis*, it has been one of the greatest boons to mankind in all the history of medicine.

The elements of blood itself have fascinated men ever since the microscope permitted a detailed look at them. One of the first to discover a blood component was Malpighi, not long after he spotted the capillaries which had eluded Harvey. Some 300 years later, for all the intervening refinements in detection techniques, many mysteries remain about the makeup of the blood and the functions of certain parts of it.

Components of a quartet

Blood has four main components. About 55 per cent of it is a fluid, plasma. The remaining 45 per cent is made up of three kinds of cells: red cells, or erythocytes, Malpighi's find; white cells, or leukocytes; and platelets, or thrombocytes. Except for one variety of white blood cells, all the cellular components are manufactured in the bone marrow.

Plasma, in which the cells float, is a yellowish solution, 92 per cent water, the other 8 per cent a host of substances indispensable to life. Among them are nutriments—glucose, fats and amino acids; inorganic materials like sodium, potassium and calcium; special proteins like fibrinogen, albumin and various globulins; antibodies, defensive globulins which fight off viruses and other unwelcome intruders in the body; and hormones such as insulin and epinephrine, more familiarly known as adrenalin, which speeds up the heart rate whenever some emergency requires a greater blood flow to the muscles. With its potent arsenal to draw upon, plasma plays a crucial role in maintaining the body's chemical balance, water content and temperature at a safe level—a function quite apart from its role in the transport of food, oxygen and waste.

The red cells outnumber the white cells 700 to 1. Theirs is the exclusive and all-important job of picking up oxygen in the lungs, carrying it to the rest of the body and convoying waste carbon dioxide back the other way. Their life is hectic and short; after about three or four months they fall apart and are replaced by new recruits sent into the blood-stream from the bone marrow. The red cells' effectiveness as an oxygen-carrier is due to their content of hemoglobin, a compound of protein and iron which gives blood its red color. Hemoglobin has a chemical way of latching onto oxygen and holding it in its grip until destination is reached. Because oxygen does not dissolve well in plasma, the binding power of hemoglobin is vital. Otherwise the blood could carry only enough dissolved oxygen for two and a half seconds, and any period of breathlessness, such as the brief time after a sneeze, might well prove fatal. When, for any reason, the hemoglobin content dips below minimum body needs, the result is anemia, meaning, although not quite literally, "no blood." A diet deficient in iron-rich foods, such as meat, may cause anemia in truck drivers as well as in frail old ladies.

A rally of wrigglers

The white cells constitute the blood's mobile guard. Some are endowed with the curious ability to wriggle out of the bloodstream and back in again. They rally in great numbers wherever invading bacteria gain entry into the body, engulfing and destroying them. Whenever white cells mobilize for action, the body compensates by manufacturing more. Double the usual number may appear in the blood within hours. Often this rising white count, as doctors describe it, serves as an early tip-off to dangerous infections.

Perhaps the strangest of blood's three cellular components are the platelets, named for their resemblance to tiny plates. For a long while these cells, discovered about a century ago, utterly baffled researchers. Then it was observed that people with low platelet counts were especially vulnerable to bleeding. Platelets are thus vital to blood-clotting. When they touch the roughened surface of a torn blood vessel, they burst apart, releasing chemicals that set off a reaction in the blood leaking out. The exact steps are still in dispute, but the result is the conversion of one of plasma's proteins, fibrinogen, into a network of crystals that enmesh the red blood cells—thereby forming a clot which seals the leak.

In its basic operations blood finds a powerful ally in the substance known as lymph. This watery fluid, as mentioned earlier, serves as a bridge across which oxygen, nutriments and wastes pass between the capillaries and the body cells. As the bloodstream unloads its offgoing cargoes through the capillaries, many of its plasma proteins—fully half of them in the course of a day—also escape, under the force of blood pressure. Once they have broken out, the errant proteins cannot get back directly into the bloodstream. The lymph, therefore, takes a hand. It convoys them—via a special circulatory system of its own, composed of lymphatic capillaries and ducts—into veins near the shoulders, which pass them

PERCENTAGE OF WATER IN TISSUES

Fat	20
Blood	80
Bone	25-30
Connective	60
Kidney	80
Liver	70
Muscle (Striated)	75
Skin	70
Nervous Tissue:	
Gray Matter	85
White Matter	70

THE HUMAN RESERVOIR
If it were possible to drain all the water from a 200-pound man, his dehydrated body would weigh a mere 80 pounds. This table shows where much of the body water is distributed. There is no more water in the blood than in some so-called "solid" tissues. Turkish-bath habitués will be chagrined to learn that there is less water in fat than in any other tissue, including bone. The greatest proprietors of water are the cells of tissues.

into the heart. Lymph also carries along a number of chemical products, including droplets of fat and cholesterol which are absorbed during the process of digestion. By the time the meandering and relatively sluggish lymphatic system brings these cargoes back to the heart, they have been greatly diluted.

The performance of the lymph, and of the blood itself, has been largely revealed within our own century. Today, for example, it is commonplace knowledge that an individual possesses either blood type A, B, AB or O. It was only in 1900 that the existence of various blood types was established; the discoverer was an Austrian physician, Dr. Karl Landsteiner, who later won the Nobel Prize for his work. His research was the inevitable outcome of centuries of trial-and-error in blood transfusions. The transfusion technique was a probable offshoot of the early custom of drinking blood as a means of rejuvenation; the Romans, for example, would rush into the arena to quaff the blood of dying gladiators. The first transfusion on record was effected in 1667, by Jean Baptiste Denis, physician to Louis XIV of France. Denis temporarily restored a dying boy by injecting about eight ounces of lamb's blood into his veins. In time, transfusion attempts became more widespread. But why some worked, and why some failed, or even proved fatal, was a question that continued to perplex doctors until Landsteiner.

Answers in a test tube

The simple technique which Landsteiner used to reach an answer was to mix, in test tubes, the plasma of one person with the red cells of another. In some cases the two blended smoothly; in others, the cells would not mix, clumping together instead. Inside the body such clumping would clog the capillaries—a dangerous and perhaps deadly situation. The key to clumping or not clumping, Landsteiner found, was the way red cells containing a particular protein, or agglutinogen, reacted to plasma containing another type of protein called an agglutinin. Red cells with one type of protein would be compatible with plasma containing one type of agglutinin, but not with plasma containing another type.

Landsteiner accordingly typed human blood as A, B or O (for zero). The red cells of this latter type contained no agglutinogens at all, and could thus provide a blend with any type of plasma; hence a type-O person became known as a "universal donor." The next year, two other researchers, one a pupil of Landsteiner, found a fourth blood type, AB, whose plasma would receive any type of red cell; hence a type-AB person became known as a "universal recipient." In 1940, four decades after his original discovery, Landsteiner, now an American citizen, discovered in collaboration with Dr. Alexander S. Wiener a new substance in the red cells which they labeled the Rh factor, after the rhesus monkey whose

A TRANSFUSION, 1667

In the first known successful transfusion of blood to a human, Jean Baptiste Denis, a 17th Century French physician, drained lamb's blood into the arm of a boy suffering from fever. When the boy revived, Denis tried it on another patient, as shown in this 1667 print. The patient reportedly went directly to a tavern to celebrate; he died shortly thereafter. Both Church and state outlawed transfusion and a century passed before it was tried again.

plasma they mixed with human red cells. It was found that when a mother who lacked the Rh factor, and was thus "Rh-negative," gave birth to a baby who was "Rh-positive," the infant would sometimes die.

Other new factors, whose behavior is still unclear, have also been detected in the blood, and new complexities of other sorts have been revealed about it. As often in medical science, the deeper the probe has gone the less simple the answers begin to be. The same is true for the heart, which in recent decades has been subject to inspection, manipulation and operation to an extent William Harvey and his successors would never in their wildest dreams have imagined to be possible.

The gamble of the scalpel

Early attempts to treat heart defects with surgery were limited and gingerly. No surgeon dared enter the heart itself for fear of starting massive bleeding or causing the heart to stop. Eminent heart specialists violently opposed the mere idea that the heart might be approached by the scalpel. Nevertheless the risks began to be taken.

Progress depended, however, on diagnostic methods which would help the surgeon pin down the precise kind of damage involved. The basic technique was pioneered in 1929 by a young German doctor, Werner Forssmann, in an experiment so hair-raising that colleagues regarded him as a lunatic. Forssmann had passed a thin rubber catheter—tube— through the arm vein of a cadaver and into the heart itself. He decided to try this on himself. His first attempt failed; the doctor assisting him lost his nerve halfway. Forssmann repeated the effort alone, as a nurse stood by. With fluoroscope and mirror, he followed the catheter's progress up his own arm vein. When he had inserted the tube 20 inches, its tip entered his right atrium. But he knew that no one would believe what he had done unless he could produce unassailable evidence. With the catheter still in place, he walked down a long corridor and up two flights of stairs to have X-rays made as proof of his achievement. This extraordinary experiment was reported in an obscure journal. It went unheeded until two Americans—Dr. Dickinson W. Richards and Dr. André Cournand—recognized in it the diagnostic technique that heart surgeons needed, and developed it into commonplace procedure. Subsequently they and Forssmann jointly received the Nobel Prize for their work.

Prolonged surgery deep inside the heart requires a "dry"—bloodless— field in which to work. This problem was met by the invention of the heart-lung machine, whose workings are illustrated on pages 130 and 131. Hooked up to the patient's circulatory system, this machine shunts the blood away from the heart, oxygenates it artificially and pumps it back into the general circulation, all while the surgeon does his repair work uninterrupted. Inevitably, the uses of technology have been extended to the development of artificial parts for the heart. Doctors themselves have been responsible for two of the most remarkable. To duplicate the normal impulse of the cardiac pacemaker—the sinus node—Dr. Adrian Kantrowitz of New York, collaborating with electronics engineers, developed a battery-powered device hooked up by wires inside the wearer's body. Plastic valves to replace damaged heart valves have been devised both by Dr. Charles Hufnagel of Georgetown University and by Dr. Albert Starr of Portland, Oregon. In February 1963, Dr. Starr successfully replaced three damaged valves in the same patient's heart simultaneously. In his view, the development of an entire, workable artificial heart is no longer a surgical but an engineering problem.

Today no aspect of the circulatory system escapes the exploratory eye of the medical scientist and technologist. Spurring their efforts is the awareness that some of the most basic questions about the circulatory system remain unanswered. We do not yet know precisely what causes high blood pressure, hardening of the arteries and heart attacks. The part played in the onset of such ailments by the celebrated cholesterol— a fatty substance carried by the blood—is yet to be settled. We are far from sure of the origin of some blood cells. Indeed, we do not know why the heart itself beats. Enough mystery still hovers about the circulatory system to preoccupy legions of heart researchers for decades to come.

Blood, Circulation— and Life

Among all the body's systems, the blood is unique: it is the only fluid tissue. This fluid, endlessly coursing from the heart to the remotest parts of the body and returning, is a sea in which the body is bathed. Every cell is an island that could not exist without the blood and its derivative lymph, which surround it. Pumped by the heart *(opposite)*, the blood delivers the food and the oxygen that combine in the cells to produce energy; then it carries away the waste produced by the cells. It carries off excess heat generated by the internal organs to be dissipated through the skin. It distributes the regulatory hormones that govern, among other things, physical growth and reproduction. And it delivers the agents that fight disease and those that rebuild tissue damaged by disease or accident. The safe transfer of blood and its vital qualities from one person to another has been among the most important developments of modern medicine.

A FIST-SIZED PUMP
The endless circling of the blood depends upon one tireless muscle: the heart *(opposite)*. Though it is only about the size of the fist and weighs a half to three quarters of a pound, the heart does enough work each day to lift the body a mile straight up. In this frontal view of the organ, an injection of pigment gives color to the web of veins, arteries and capillaries that serve the heart.

The Blood Vessels, Large and Small

The raw materials for the energy that powers man's every thought and action are transported in the blood. The enriched blood is carried in a network of tiny vessels, capillaries, to each cell. These capillaries are so small that 60 long ones or 120 short ones would stretch only the length of this line of type. Yet there are so many capillaries in the body that, laid end to end, they would ring the equator more than twice.

Blood coming into the capillaries from the arteries has been loaded with oxygen in the lungs or with food from the digestive system. The walls of the capillaries are only one cell thick; so thin that the nutrient-laden blood is able, by osmosis and diffusion, to pass its oxygen and food to the body's cells and to receive from the cells their waste. The spent blood then flows from the capillaries into the veins, which direct it back to the heart. In the heart the blood enters the arteries and is carried by them to the lungs and digestive system, to be aerated and enriched again before returning to the capillaries.

The body's largest blood vessels, the aorta and the pulmonary artery, are about an inch in diameter. Arteries have thick elastic walls, the pulsations of which assist the heart in pumping. Vein walls are more rigid. Many of them, particularly in the lower part of the body, have valves which prevent a backflow of blood.

AN INNER VIEW
A television camera photographs the retina of the eye through an ophthalmoscope and projects the image on a screen *(right)*. Thus, the eye provides a window for examining the flow of living blood inside the body. The retina, the innermost layer of the wall of the eyeball, shows orange on the screen; the blood vessels appear as red and the optic nerve is seen as yellow.

BLOOD IN THE EYE

A closer view *(left)* of the retina as seen by the television camera *(opposite)* shows the blood vessels branching out to serve all cells. In addition to capillaries, arterioles and venules—the small arteries and veins that connect with the capillaries—are shown. The brighter and narrower of the two are the arterioles. The area from which the vessels emanate is the optic disk.

A MUSCULAR TUBE

This cross section of a venule, or small vein, shows its inner layer of elastic membrane in brown and its muscles in red. In the living organism the blood would flow in the irregular, flattened hole in the center. The photograph has been enlarged 250 times. Venules collect blood from the capillaries and carry it to even larger veins which transport it to the heart.

A State of Mutual Dependency

Blood is indispensable to every cell of the body. The need for its vital supplies is so universal that even blood vessels have blood vessels. Blood sustains even those organs by which it is, itself, sustained—the heart, the stomach, the lungs, the intestines.

The stomach *(right)* helps to prepare the food that the blood carries to all parts of the body. After the food has been reduced to particles that are small enough to enter the bloodstream, it is received by the blood through the permeable walls of the villi *(lower right)* which line the inside of the small intestine.

The lungs *(below)*, which have the densest congregation of capillaries of any part of the body, load oxygen into the blood. The blood, in turn, releases in the lungs for exhalation the waste carbon dioxide it has received from cells everywhere in the body.

THE STOMACH
A mass of blood vessels supplies the stomach *(above)* with nutrients. The larger arteries *(red)* and the veins *(blue)* occur in mutually entwined pairs. The smaller capillaries, through which the stomach's cells receive the food and oxygen they need to live, also are shown in red.

THE LUNGS
Bright red capillaries cover a human lung *(left)* like clumps of moss. The larger arteries and veins are shown in red and blue respectively. Each lung has about 375 million alveoli, or air pouches. Capillaries largely compose the walls of the alveoli and take fresh oxygen from them.

THE INTESTINE

Villi of the small intestine *(pink)* pass nutrients from the digestive system to the blood vessels *(blue)*. These tiny fingers extending into the intestine are shown here magnified about 100 times. They increase the absorptive surface of the intestine to about 30 square yards.

91

THE OXYGEN CARRIERS

Red corpuscles (salmon-colored at right) cluster in a blood sample. Carriers of the blood's oxygen, these cells are not capable of moving themselves but are swept along by the flow of the blood, frequently stacking up like plates. They are manufactured in the marrow of bones.

THE FIGHTING CELLS

White corpuscles are stained violet in the photograph below. Unlike the red corpuscles, white cells have a nucleus, usually fragmented. Also, they can move independently of the blood flow when pursuing bacteria. A red cell is seen edge on between two white cells in the upper left.

10 Pints of Vital Fluid

The blood teems with life. Billions of cells float about carrying oxygen, repairing leaks and fighting bacteria. In the average man, eight million blood cells die every second and are replaced by new cells produced in the bone marrow, lymph glands and lymphoid tissues of the tonsils, spleen, thymus and intestine.

The cells swim in the plasma, which also carries food, antibodies, hormones, clotting agents and wastes. Plasma is practically all water and makes up a little more than half the volume of the blood. In an average man with 10 pints of blood, about five and a half pints are plasma.

Red corpuscles *(opposite, above)*, 25 trillion of them, occupy about four and a half pints. These cells contain hemoglobin, an iron compound that can pick up more than half its own weight in oxygen. They start life with a diameter of perhaps nine 10,000ths of an inch, shrink at maturity to three 10,000ths and break up after about 120 days.

White cells *(opposite, below)* and platelets make up the remaining volume of the blood. Platelets, which live only for two to four days, outnumber the larger white cells by 1.5 trillion to 35 billion, but are so small they fill only two teaspoons. Their tendency to adhere to whatever they touch fits them for the job of repairing leaks. The white corpuscles fight infection by eating bacterial invaders *(below)*.

START | 10 SECONDS | 20 SECONDS | 30 SECONDS

A white corpuscle begins to attack a bacillus that threatens the body with disease. Ten seconds later it starts to ingest the invader.

40 SECONDS | 50 SECONDS | 60 SECONDS | 70 SECONDS

Within 70 seconds the white cell has completely absorbed the attacker. These photographs are shown enlarged about 2,000 times.

The Rich Mine of Plasma

In using blood to treat certain conditions, doctors have found that in some cases the parts are greater than the whole. Certain types of blood cannot be mixed in transfusions, for example, without forming potentially fatal clots of red corpuscles. But plasma—which is blood with all the cells removed—can be administered to anyone. This, plus its usefulness in fighting shock, made plasma a major weapon in treating battle wounds during World War II. Also in the 1940s, a Harvard research group headed by Edwin J. Cohn developed ways to extract and purify parts of plasma, each of which combats specific conditions.

Albumin, for example, fights shock by preventing hemorrhages. Gamma globulin, carrying antibodies built up to fight viruses and bacteria, confers, at least temporarily, the donor's immunity to measles and certain kinds of hepatitis or infantile paralysis upon another person. Fibrinogen, which is essential to natural blood-clotting, is used to control bleeding in surgery.

The usefulness of these agents is heightened by the fact that they can be frozen or powdered, and stored for months *(right)*. And Cohn increased the supply of plasma. He developed a system for extracting only plasma from donors *(far right)*. The body replaces plasma faster than it replaces whole blood—hence donors can give plasma more often than whole blood.

A STOREHOUSE OF SPECIFICS
A technician in a cold-storage vault of the Harvard Medical School fills a jar with a powdered blood fraction extracted from plasma. Such supplies can be collected and stored over long periods. Just as chemists have developed a wide variety of fuels from petroleum, so medical researchers have derived from plasma a series of products useful for specific conditions.

Donated plasma goes into the sack on the left; corpuscles are returned to donor's body.

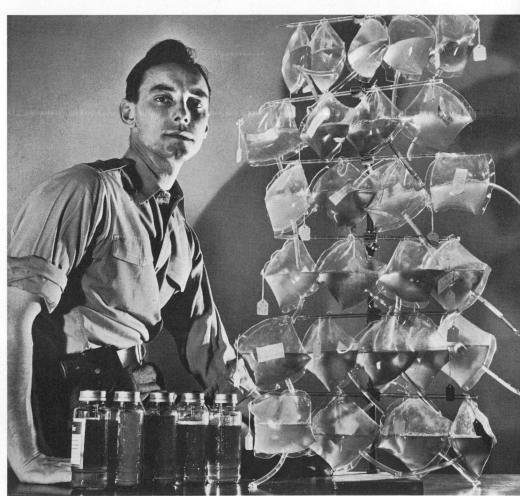

INCREASING THE OUTPUT

The plastic bags hold 26 pints of plasma that Patrolman Louis Ruskey gave in one year. The five pint bottles contain the whole blood he could have given safely in the same time. A centrifuge separated his blood as it was taken from him and returned to him all but the plasma.

The Red Cells and Flash Freezing

While plasma is invaluable in many cases, there are times when nothing but whole blood will suffice for transfusions. However, despite the widespread establishment of blood banks, whole-blood transfusions remain costly. One reason is that blood cannot be preserved for more than three weeks, because red cells deteriorate outside the body. Thus, banks constantly need new supplies. An answer to the problem may be found in techniques in cryobiology (from the Greek, *kryos:* icy cold) such as shown at left and on the opposite page.

Red cells cannot be frozen in any normal way because their water content forms ice crystals that puncture the cells. But in 1949, the Reverend Basile J. Luyet, a Swiss-born priest working at Saint Louis University in Missouri, found he could preserve 70 per cent of the cells of ox blood by dropping its temperature to −202°F. in a second's time. This turned the water into an amorphous solid rather than crystals. Others followed in attempts to flash freeze the blood.

One investigation showed that cellular water could be replaced with glycerol, which freezes without crystallizing. However, it is difficult to get glycerol out when the blood is needed. Dr. Charles Huggins Jr. of Harvard reported in 1963 he had solved the problem. Instead of glycerol, he used dimethylsulfoxide, which washes out of thawed cells easily *(left)*.

FROZEN ASSETS

Dr. Harold Meryman, a pioneer cryobiologist, conducts an experiment at the Naval Medical Research Institute in Bethesda, Maryland, to improve the techniques for flash freezing of blood. Dr. Meryman has also developed a method of freezing whole animals, thereby supplying a way of preserving museum specimens that may someday replace the dying art of taxidermy.

A CLEANSING BATH

Thawed red corpuscles in the plastic bag are washed clean of the chemical preservative that was used in freezing them. The machine is no larger than a suitcase and can process five pints every 20 minutes. The system, which has been used in many human transfusion cases at the Massachusetts General Hospital, promises to cut the cost of transfusions substantially.

5

Fueling
the Body's
Machinery

MORE THAN CAN BE ACCURATELY MEASURED, medical advance has hinged on individual case histories. Down through time many men and women have contributed to the mainstream of our knowledge of health and disease through maladies privately endured and often not overcome. For the most part their identities are beyond recall. Among the rare exceptions is the name of Alexis St. Martin, a 19th Century French-Canadian fur trader who was destined to provide posterity with its first real insight into the workings of the human digestive system.

St. Martin's case history was so unusual that when he died in 1880, William Osler, then dean of American medicine, tried to buy his stomach as an exhibit for the Army Medical Museum in Washington. To the disappointment of the medical fraternity, the deceased man's family insisted that it be buried with the rest of his body. But in the long run the failure to preserve this relic mattered far less than the fact that St. Martin's doctor, William Beaumont, was a man who seized a unique opportunity when he saw it, and kept meticulous records to describe what he had done about it. An essential page was added to the annals of medicine because of a one-in-a-million chance which brought together, on the lonely American frontier, a rare medical phenomenon and a doctor with a genius for painstaking observation.

One June day in 1822, at a trading post on the Michigan-Canadian border, St. Martin was struck by an accidental shotgun blast which tore a great gaping hole in his left side. Beaumont, a young Army surgeon, arrived from nearby Fort Mackinac to treat him. Certain that his patient would be dead within 36 hours, Beaumont dressed the wound as best he could. But St. Martin, aged 18 at the time, survived and healed, although a tunnel two and a half inches around remained open in his side, leading directly through skin and muscle into the stomach. When he had fully recuperated, he was able to resume his usual vigorous pursuits, simply covering his wound with layers of gauze.

St. Martin's fistula (false opening) was not unique in history. A similar case had been reported as far back as 1530. Beaumont, however, was the first doctor to realize that the fistula could be used as a peephole to watch the digestive system in action—a process hitherto hidden to the eye. With astonishing persistence, lacking a laboratory or skilled help, he made a number of investigations of inestimable value to his profession ever since.

Long before Beaumont, physicians had realized that food, once taken in, must undergo radical transformation before it could serve to sustain the body. They knew that it was chewed and ground in the mouth, and lubricated by saliva. They also knew that it passed from the throat into the stomach by way of a narrow, 10-inch-long channel, the esophagus, named after the Greek word which means "to carry what is eaten."

CORNUCOPIA MIDWESTERN-STYLE

Harvest-time helpers join a Kansas farmer at a noonday dinner of fried chicken, cranberry sauce, pickles, potatoes with gravy, chocolate cake and fruit. While the digestive system might be expected to quail under this onslaught, the rugged labors of these diners help them burn off the fuel into which the food is converted, and permit another imposing meal by nightfall.

A HUMAN MOLAR IN CROSS SECTION

ENAMEL

DENTIN

PULP

GUM

CEMENTUM

PERIDENTAL MEMBRANE

BLOOD VESSELS
AND NERVES

The exposed portion is called the clinical crown and is covered by enamel, the hardest substance in the body. Below the gums, the root is covered with softer cementum. Beneath the layer of bonelike dentin is the pulp, which houses the nerves and blood vessels. The tooth is attached to the jawbone by the peridental membrane, a tough connective tissue.

But what happened once the food reached the stomach? For centuries, popular belief held that it simply putrefied there. The first hint of the real answer came in the early 1700s. A French scientist, René de Réaumur, performed a series of experiments with a pet bird—a kite—which led to a major revelation. Kites have the protective habit of regurgitating anything they cannot digest. Réaumur lowered tiny pieces of sponge into his bird's stomach. When they came up, he found that they had absorbed a juice so potent that, as test-tube trials proved, it would dissolve bits of meat into liquid. His discovery persuaded physiologists that digestion was initiated by a secretion produced inside the stomach. But no one had a chance to observe the stomach at work until St. Martin's accident and, as Beaumont described it, "a concurrence of circumstances which probably never can again occur."

Beaumont's excitement was reflected in his notebooks. "When he lies on the opposite side," he wrote, "I can look directly into the cavity of the Stomach, and almost see the process of digestion. . . ." One of Beaumont's techniques was to attach pieces of food to a length of thread and lower it, through the fistula, into the stomach. By withdrawing the food when it was partly digested, he confirmed that the stomach did, indeed, secrete a powerful digestive juice. By further painstaking studies, Beaumont was able to draw some 50 "inferences," as he called them, about the gastrointestinal system, among them that the stomach acted the same way no matter what the diet, that bulk as well as nutriment was necessary in food intake, that "stimulating condiments" were harmful to the stomach, and that "the use of ardent spirits always produces disease of the stomach, if persevered in."

Vagaries of a guinea pig

St. Martin, a morose man at best, sometimes grew restive in his role as guinea pig. At one point he simply disappeared from his usual haunts for four years; patiently Beaumont tracked him down. They continued their collaboration, on and off, for eight years. During that time, St. Martin enjoyed excellent health. His appetite was good, and his food did not have to be pre-softened or otherwise specially prepared. He was able to work as a handyman and engage in such strenuous exertions as chopping wood. Ironically, he outlived Beaumont by 27 years, dying at 76.

The conclusions which Beaumont drew about the way food passes through the body provided the guidelines for the extensive research which inevitably followed. The path of the food lies along the gastrointestinal tract—GI tract for short—a channel so coiled and twisted upon itself that it winds and bends for almost 30 feet from the top of the esophagus to the anus. Like other natural functions, such as the coursing of blood through the veins or the healing of a broken bone, digestion proceeds without any direction on our part. We may consciously decide to chew or not to chew, but we cannot, at will, influence the activity of our salivary glands. As the food is swallowed—mainly by reflex action—it passes altogether beyond our control. Automatically, muscular contractions triggered by the act of swallowing close off three possible routes the food might take: back into the mouth, up into the nasal cavity or into the windpipe. Only one route is left open—down the esophagus and into the stomach.

Food requires no help from gravity to make its way down the coiled pathway; an astronaut's digestive system works very well indeed in a condition of zero gravity. The motive power is furnished by muscles which stretch the full length of the tract. They form two layers, one running along the tract and the other encircling it in concentric rings. Both by setting up a churning motion, and by a series of progressive contractions known as peristaltic waves, the twin sets of muscles force food all the way from the throat to the rectum, much as if toothpaste were being squeezed along its tube by some built-in power in the tube walls.

The proportionate pouch

Most people think that the stomach is situated near the navel. It lies much higher in the abdomen, on the left side, nested up under the diaphragm and protected by the rib cage. In form, it is a kind of pouch, about 10 inches long, with a diameter that depends on its content. When full, it can stretch to hold as much as two quarts of food. When empty, it collapses on itself like a deflated balloon.

The processing which food undergoes, once it is eaten, is a rugged one. Conceivably there might be fewer gourmets, and fewer cases of obesity, if the digestive process were visible, or if its clinical detailing in television commercials were more closely heeded. A quickly gulped tuna on rye and a slowly savored beef à la Bourguignonne meet the same inexorable fate: whatever the food, it is mashed, churned, pulverized and generally battered beyond recognition. But it is only by these gyrations that the digestive system manifests its efficiency, and ensures our physical energy, our freedom from potentially noxious wastes and, in fact, our repeated ability to indulge in the joys of the appetite.

Whether slated to be converted into energy or to be eliminated as waste, ingested food materials take the same route along the gastrointestinal tract for five sixths of the way. Arriving at the entrance of the stomach from the esophagus, the food has already been softened. Its entry into the stomach—as well as its exit therefrom—is regulated by circular muscles which act somewhat like purse strings, alternately expanding and contracting. The stomach itself works on the food both mechanically and chemically. The movement of the stomach walls mashes

TEETH AND THEIR JOBS

These teeth are the right-hand half, upper and lower jaws, of an adult's set of 32, which gradually push out a child's 20 milk teeth between the approximate ages of six and 17. The adult can chew up nuts and meat with his molars (1, 2 and 3), grind food for swallowing with the premolars (4 and 5), rip into skin with his canines (6), and nip off a stem and nibble into the cheek of an apple with his incisors (7 and 8).

101

it further, kneading it as a cook kneads dough. This also permits the thorough mixing-in of a digestive juice whose chief ingredients are pepsin and hydrochloric acid.

Pepsin is one of at least 700 varieties of enzymes known to exist in the human body. Each of these complicated organic compounds has its own particular task to perform, but all function as catalysts to speed up chemical reactions. By a neat coincidence, the first enzyme, diastase, was discovered in 1833—the year Beaumont was beginning to write up his experiments on St. Martin—when two French chemists, Anselme Payen and Jean Persoz, found a substance in the human body which helped transform starch into sugar. Later other enzymes were found that help break down other foods besides starches, and others that have many nondigestive duties as well. Without enzymes, in short, bodily functions would proceed far too slowly to sustain life.

Dozens of different enzymes participate directly in the digestive process alone. Among them, pepsin serves to break down the protein in food in the stomach. It can act, however, only in the presence of the hydrochloric acid, which helps soften the food. Hydrochloric acid is such a strong corrosive that it will eat its way straight through a cotton handkerchief, yet it does no harm to the stomach walls. A film of sticky mucus, lining the walls, protects them against the acid.

A gatekeeper on duty

All this activity represents only one function of the stomach, however. Its principal role is as a storage tank where food can be kept until the next section of the GI tract, the small intestine, is ready to receive it. The small intestine processes food in very small quantities at a time. To keep it from being overwhelmed, food is allowed into it under control of the circular muscle at the lower end of the stomach—aptly labeled pylorus, the Latin for "gatekeeper." It is the action of this muscle that enables us to eat large meals hours apart; otherwise we would have to nibble small snacks at brief intervals. By expanding and contracting just so much, the pylorus keeps the small intestine in a state of balance.

The small intestine is the longest section of the GI tract, twisting and coiling for more than 20 feet. Here the essential chemical reactions which break food down begin in earnest. The first section of the small intestine is the duodenum, 10 to 11 inches long. This segment got its name from the Latin for "twelve," owing to the fact that its span was originally measured by finger widths instead of by inches. In the duodenum the hydrochloric acid in the food arriving from the stomach is neutralized by alkaline digestive juices. Some of these juices come from the pancreas, a soft, pink gland which lies below and behind the stomach; some come from the liver, the heaviest organ in the body, a dark red gland situated below the lower right side of the rib cage.

With the acid neutralized, the chemical breakdown of food moves into high gear. As the food is forced along the duodenum, it is like a man running a gauntlet. It undergoes constant bombardment; any scrap that happens to escape one assault runs into another farther on. The attackers are the most powerful of all the digestive enzymes. By contrast, the impact of pepsin in the stomach, or of preceding enzymes in the mouth, is minor. Indeed, a man whose stomach has been removed by surgery can still satisfactorily digest his food if it is properly chewed. But the stoppage of enzymatic action in the duodenum could be critical.

Once through the duodenum, the battered food particles face final disintegration. This takes place in the second and third sections of the small intestine, the jejunum and the ilium. Proteins in the food are broken down into amino acids; carbohydrates into molecules of glucose (sugar); and fats into fatty acids and glycerol.

During the course of this chemical Armageddon, perhaps the most fascinating microcosmic structures in the human body, seldom known to the layman, come into play. These are tiny, soft, hairlike projections called villi, which protrude in countless millions from the lining of the jejunum and ilium like nap from a Turkish towel. Minute as they are, the villi, named for the Latin for "tuft of hair," perform a function of incalculable importance. This is the separation of the valuable particles of protein and sugar and fat from a number of waste ingredients such as cellulose—a component of raw fruits and vegetables which humans cannot digest. The villi thus mark the parting of the ways for the useful nutrients and the useless materials in the foods we eat during the course of a day.

The errant orange pit

Serving as a vast, velvety filter, the villi wave the waste on into the colon, or large intestine, where it is forced through to the rectum and, by a series of final peristaltic contractions, expelled from the body. Occasionally, in moving from small intestine to colon, some small bit of waste, like an orange pit, will sneak out of the main digestive stream and lodge in the vestigial organ known as the appendix, which is situated at the upper end of the colon. Such strays can cause inflammation of the appendix and necessitate its removal.

While the villi are dispatching the waste one way, they are sending the beneficial amino acids, sugars and fats other ways. The fats move into the special circulatory system described in the previous chapter, the lymphatic vessels, which send them into the bloodstream to be diluted, and thence to go wherever needed in the body. The amino acids and sugars are passed along the capillaries of the blood through the

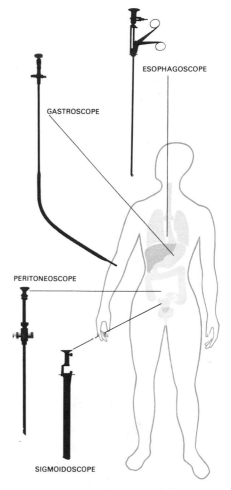

TOOLS THAT SEE INTO THE BODY

Four of the many optical instruments that can be inserted into the body for direct observation are illustrated above. The esophagoscope is used in diagnosing diseases of the esophagus. The gastroscope is a flexible tube rigged with a series of lenses to examine the inside of the stomach. The peritoneoscope is inserted through the abdominal wall to study intestinal disorders, and the sigmoidoscope is used in diagnosing diseases of the rectum.

103

great portal vein into the liver, there to be converted into a form usable by the cells of the body.

The liver's primacy as the chemical capital of the body was intuitively suspected long before it was actually confirmed. Among our elders the term "liverish" is still used to document any vague feeling of internal discomfort. Through the ages many powers have been ascribed to the liver. It was thought to be the seat of the soul, of love, of desire and of courage (hence the epithet "lily-livered"). It was also believed to produce yellow bile, one of the body's "four humors" that were supposed to determine health and disease; when bile predominated among this quartet, the occupant of the body in question was presumed to be hopelessly bad-tempered.

Safety in a surplus

The liver does, indeed, manufacture bile. It is also, by far, the most versatile of all organs in the body, so indispensable that without it the body would perish within 24 hours. In addition to its part in the digestive process, it filters old red cells from the blood; it acts as a general detoxifier for the body, removing chemicals and drugs taken in from the outside; it manufactures other complex chemicals needed by the body, such as blood proteins and cholesterol; and it synthesizes lipids—a kind of fatty material—which, among other functions, help form insulating sheaths about nerve fibers. As if to compensate for the rash placement of so many eggs in one basket, the body is provided with a vast surplus of liver tissue. We can limp along reasonably well if as little as a fourth of the liver is performing normally. Moreover, it has remarkable recuperative qualities; when one part is damaged, it tends to grow new cells to replace the lost ones.

In the digestive process the liver's role is in the nature of a follow-up. All the way down the GI tract, the digestive process consists of breaking food down. In the liver the process is reversed. The sugar is built up into a new substance, a special body fuel called glycogen. The sole function of glycogen is to provide a convenient, compact form of storage for glucose, which, in its own form, would take up too much room. As the body requires additional nourishment, the liver reconverts the glycogen to glucose, releasing it, bit by bit, into the bloodstream. The liver is thus also responsible, in part, for maintaining the level of sugar in the blood.

Parallel to the processing of sugar in the liver, another vital transformation takes place with the amino acids, the fundamental units of protein. These are rearranged into the body's building blocks, for continuing use in the regeneration of its cells. Every part of the body enjoys this service, and with impressive speed. The lining of the entire GI tract itself, for example, is renewed every three days. The blood carries the

THE MIRACLE OF METABOLISM
The remarkable process by which all cells convert food into energy *(below)* or prepare it for storage for later use *(opposite)* is shown here in simplified drawings. During conversion, or oxidation, fatty acids, amino acids and glucose are ground down by enzymes. After nitrogen wastes in the amino acids are eliminated, the rest undergoes a cycle of combustion, named for its identifier as the Krebs cycle. From this it emerges in the form of carbon dioxide, water and the energy needed for the body's work.

GLUCOSE
NITROGEN
AMINO ACIDS
FATTY ACIDS

NITROGEN PRODUCTS

CARBON DIOXIDE (CO$_2$)

WATER (H$_2$O)

ENERGY

FOOD PRODUCTS   ENZYME BREAKDOWN   KREBS CYCLE

104

converted foodstuffs to the body's cells, which transform them into both structural units and energy. It is this transformation which is the ultimate goal of each of the intricate stages in the digestive process.

Although the digestive system works without any conscious intervention, its enormously elaborate mechanism is coordinated and controlled by the nervous system. This is done through a complex network of nerve cells which relay messages back and forth between the GI tract and the brain. We cannot, by an act of will, interfere with this relay system. But through it, without our ever being aware of the fact, the digestive machinery can be heavily influenced by the reactions induced by emotions such as anger or fear, tension or insecurity.

The existence of a relationship between the emotions and digestion has been known for centuries. The dry mouth or the empty sensation at the pit of the stomach caused by fear, the heavy stomach that accompanies depression, the cramping pain of tension—these are sensations which all of us have shared. Beaumont, that indefatigable observer, noted that anger and excitement produced physical changes in his patient's stomach. But it was not until the early 1940s that a detailed, systematic investigation was carried out to trace the precise physical effects which emotional reactions can bring on in the digestive tract. As with Beaumont, the doctors who made this second historic investigation were able to do so as the result of an accident which left its victim with a fistula into his stomach. Unlike Beaumont, they did not have immediate access to the victim; almost half a century elapsed before they even encountered him.

The clam chowder chronicle

In 1895 a nine-year-old boy, memorialized in medical chronicles simply as Tom, swallowed some steaming-hot clam chowder under the impression that it was beer. The chowder seared his esophagus and blocked it off from his stomach. Tom was rushed to the hospital, where repeated efforts to unblock his esophagus failed. It was then decided to perform a gastrostomy—an operation to provide an artificial channel from the outside into the stomach which would permit the burned esophagus to be bypassed and yet allow Tom to feed himself. While he was on the operating table, however, his condition suddenly became critical, and the surgeon was forced to finish the operation hurriedly, without attempting to devise a closure. The boy pulled through, but was left with an opening into his stomach an inch and a half wide.

Tom's fistula became the dominating factor in his life. He learned to digest his food by chewing it up and then spitting it into a funnel attached to a rubber tube that led directly into his stomach. He ate only twice a day, and he had to wait for five hours between each meal, until

STORAGE FOR THE FUTURE

The cells, no wastrels, use food not converted into immediate energy to repair and rebuild worn tissues, while the excess is thriftily stored. Both call for the conversion of food products into tissue. This aspect of metabolism, called synthesis, is diagrammed below. On the left hand are fatty acids, amino acids and glucose, plus glycerol with carbon. On the right, these products are shown after they have been re-formed by a cell into the body's complex substances —fats, proteins and carbohydrates.

NITROGEN   AMINO ACIDS   FATTY ACIDS

GLYCEROL
CARBON

GLUCOSE

FOOD PRODUCTS

FAT   PROTEIN   CARBOHYDRATE

his stomach was empty; otherwise, the food would spill over. Tom soon found himself able to cope with these physical difficulties. But he was shy and sensitive, and in constant fear of embarrassment and of ridicule. As a schoolboy, his intense desire to be like everybody else drove him on to play football with particular ardor. In time he married. Only with his family and a few friends did Tom feel secure. Although scrupulously honest, he would invent all sorts of elaborate lies to avoid eating with people who were unaware of his injury.

Aftermath of a ditchdigger

For more than 30 years, Tom managed to keep his fistula a secret even from doctors, and to engage in strenuous manual labor. One day in New York, in 1939, while he was working as a ditchdigger, lifting a heavy pick every few seconds, the steady movement of the pick caused the bandage over his fistula to rub against it, making it bleed. Weakened by the loss of blood, Tom just barely made his way to a hospital. There the case of the muscular little man, now 53, came to the attention of two doctors, Stewart Wolf and Harold Wolff. Immediately they realized that within their grasp was exactly the same opportunity which Beaumont had seized more than a hundred years earlier.

Beaumont and his 19th Century successors had concentrated on the physical processes of digestion. Like many of their contemporaries, Drs. Wolf and Wolff were more interested in tracing the effects which various emotional states can have on the body. In particular, they were eager to discover whether prolonged emotional disturbance could cause serious damage to the stomach.

At first Tom was reluctant to cooperate; it took the two doctors several months to win his confidence. Their discoveries more than justified the wait. In repeated experiments, they found that certain of Tom's emotional reactions regularly triggered the same physical reactions. When he was feeling aggressive or resentful, his stomach reacted as if it were preparing to receive a meal—though in fact he had a distaste for food at the time; it secreted digestive juices, and the capillaries in the lining filled with blood, transforming it from its usual pink to a rich red. When Tom was sad, fearful, depressed or withdrawn, exactly the opposite effects occurred. The acid secretions decreased and the stomach lining became bloodless and pale. Normally, even if a person is not hungry, the introduction of food into his stomach will, through physical contact, stimulate the usual set of digestive responses. But whenever Tom was really depressed, food had no effect on his stomach at all.

It is worth noting that Tom's feelings, either of anger or of sadness, could occur both when he was hungry and when he was not hungry. In short, while emotional reactions trigger physiological reactions, these in

SMITTEN BY COLIC

The 19th Century caricaturist George Cruikshank, in a portrayal of a woman seized by colic, shows her screaming as grotesque demon dwarfs throttle her midriff. "Colic" is a generic term for an abdominal pain which can be caused by a number of disorders, including appendicitis, blockage of the ureteral passage, lead poisoning and nervous indigestion.

106

turn have no effect on appetite one way or the other. Some people, much as they need food, are unable to eat when depressed. Others continually gorge themselves as if to distract their minds from their misery. The experiments with Tom showed why either of these responses can occur; if an emotional reaction is strong enough, it will dominate appetite and hunger alike. It can also speed up the digestive process. When Tom was angry or anxious, and his gastric juices were overactive, he would digest a meal in four to five hours instead of the usual five to six.

Through their experiments, his two doctors confirmed what had long been suspected: that emotional reactions can cause too much acid to be produced by the stomach. Whenever some of this excess escapes from the stomach—carried up the esophagus with a gas bubble or down into the duodenum with the food—those sections of the digestive tract which lack a protective lining suffer accordingly. The resulting hyperacidity can cause the relatively minor annoyance of heartburn or it can seriously aggravate an ulcer.

Ulcers across the ages

Ulcers are not an exclusively modern complaint. "When there is an ulcer in the stomach or bowels," wrote Paul of Aegina, a prominent Byzantine physician of the Seventh Century A.D., "the patient must abstain from all acid food or drink." This recommended remedy almost suggests that Paul had guessed at one of the principal hallmarks of ulcers: the excess acid which can be induced by sustained overactivity of the stomach. In some cases, the amount of acid secreted may be twice that needed for digestion. Without food to neutralize it, the acid may chew away at the sticky mucus which protects the lining of the stomach, at the lining itself, or at the walls of the duodenum. The victim may receive warnings, as the ulcer develops, in the form of burning pain. If he ignores this, the ulcer can work havoc. It may eat into a blood vessel and start a hemorrhage; it may erode right through the wall of the stomach; or it may completely block the digestive process by obstructing the GI tract. And though ulcers can be healed, they are liable to recur unless something happens to change the victim's state of mind or the way in which he reacts to his life situation.

Ulcers are extremely common; they afflict between 10 and 15 per cent of the population. Much mystery still surrounds them. No one knows, for example, why they occur more frequently in the duodenum than the stomach, or why more men suffer from them than women do.

Recent research has shown that some ulcers result from a malfunction of the pituitary and adrenal glands. But these malfunctions may themselves be induced by the action of the nervous system. The enormous role played by the nervous system is demonstrated by the fact, familiar to all doctors, that the personal relationship between physician and patient is as important as any other part of the treatment of an ulcer. The ulcer patient seems to benefit as much from the doctor's interest as from any medication he might receive.

Emotional states do not, of course, cause ulcers only, or afflict only the digestive system. Their influence is evident in a host of ailments ranging all the way from skin irritations like hives and eczema to a fatal heart attack. Still, the digestive system appears at least as vulnerable as other parts of the body to emotional disturbances, both major and minor, and in this system the symptoms are more dramatic. One explanation may lie in the bulk, complexity, and copious nerve supply of the GI tract. Obviously, more things can go wrong with an intricate machine than with a simple one.

But when one considers the fantastic complexity of the digestive system, the most striking fact is that it normally operates for 24 hours a day with great efficiency. Nature, indeed, has been particularly generous in her arrangements for the ingestion and digestion of food. She has not only equipped man's body with a system that requires little assistance from his conscious mind, but has also blessed him with one of the most gratifying and universal of pleasures: that of satisfying his hunger with a hearty meal.

The Digestive Process, Step by Step

In the outline figure of the human head and torso opposite, the body's digestive system is represented as a twisted and convoluted tube. If its turns, coils and folds were straightened out, this tube would average 30 feet long in the adult. Within its length takes place an involved chemical conversion every time a gourmet meal or a bedtime snack is eaten. Here, the chemically complex foods man eats are broken down, modified and transmuted into the chemically simple substances his body must have to continue its healthy existence. But none of this involved apparatus for food conversion can work without the brain, which triggers hunger pains after measuring the level of nutrients stored in the body or by recalling to mind a memorable meal of the past. Sometimes, just the remembered smell of morning coffee is enough to start the salivary glands working. The intricate steps of digestion are explained in terms of a simplified board game.

A RESTRICTED VARIETY

While food comes in endless variety, the digestive system reduces it to the basic nutrients the body needs for fuel and building. Carbohydrates (as supplied by vegetables, fruit and bread, *opposite*) and fats (available in ice cream and meat) are converted into simple energy sources. Proteins (from meat and fish) are converted into amino acids, which are the basic building material of the body.

The Digestive System

Simple Rules to Follow

In the game of digestion at right, the players are particles of food and the board is the body. If the game were patentable, it would earn a fortune. It is fun to play—even for the board; it is healthful (if not overindulged); and it is inexpensive (if played with discretion). And it is simple to play because it is almost automated.

The mere contact of food with tissue in the mouth sends a message to the brain, which instantly orders certain glands to deliver saliva. As the teeth grind the food, the saliva lubricates it to facilitate its looping ride through the rest of the system, and also to start digesting carbohydrates.

As the teeth finish their job and the tongue helps the food along its way, care must be taken in crossing the windpipe (2). A trapdoor (the epiglottis) slams shut, forcing the food to take the indicated passageway to the next stage of the journey.

The throat connects to the esophagus, a tube leading to the stomach. By now the food has been chopped up as finely as a purée, but still needs help in moving along. So, the nerve ends of the esophagus order constrictive waves sent down the tube, forcing the food toward the stomach. This wave action is called peristalsis. In the meantime, the stomach (*following pages*) has been alerted and is already releasing gastric juices, preparing for the next move in the game.

The Digestive System

Pay here for saliva and some gastric juices. Proceed immediately to 2.

START HERE

1

Halt: wait here to be seen, smelled and tasted.

2

Wait one move to be moistened by saliva and chewed.

Draw card from "option" deck. If a carbohydrate card is chosen, start turning to sugar. Collect reward and proceed to 3.

Climb aboard esophagus for balloon ride.

3

$ Pay conductor fare for balloon journey.

Proceed to 4.

GO

Needed: A Fine Sense of Control

In the game of digestion, every player's cards are stacked and every move is precisely controlled. In the stomach (4), hydrochloric acid and the enzyme pepsin begin to break down the protein, forming simpler materials which will soon become amino acids.

On their own, the acid and the enzyme are strong enough to eat into the wall of the stomach, which is what seems to cause ulcers. Normally, these materials are not manufactured until food is present and protective mucus coats the stomach.

With a fine sense of discrimination, the stomach wall allows alcohol to escape but retains practically all other foods. The next move, to the intestines, depends on the players' readiness (carbohydrates advance faster than proteins; fats are the slowest).

Valve into stomach.

Enter stomach here.

Pause here for half hour and be churned with gastric juices.

Pay here for hydrochloric acid and pepsin. Arrange loan of lipase from intestine. Proceed to 5.

A. Proteins pause here to be broken down by acid and pepsin, collect reward and proceed to 6.

B. Milk proteins pause here to be curdled; wait our one move, then proceed to 6.

C. Small fat particles must pause, use lipase to turn into fatty acids and glycerol. Proceed to 6.

INSPECTION 6

ADMIT ONE
FREE RIDE
ALCOHOL

Alcohol wins: take free ride through body; all others pay alcohol's fare.

Partially digested food must purchase passage here for trip to duodenum. Proceed to 7.

FIRST CLASS PASSAGE
ADMIT ONE

EXCHANGE

EXCHANGE

Enter duodenum here.

7

Exchange stomach's acid for alkalinity of bile, pancreatic juice and intestinal juice. Proceed to 8.

8

Turnstile

ROUTE C

ROUTE B

ROUTE A

Caution: traffic circle ahead. Proteins take Route A. Carbohydrates take Route B. Fats take Route C.

The Digestive System

Caution: Rule Changes Ahead

When food reaches the duodenum, the first 10 inches or so of the small intestine, it has survived its test by acid. But the body switches the rules. Roughly, this is what happens: acid added in the stomach stimulates intestinal hormones which race off to the liver and pancreas. These organs send bile and pancreatic juice to the intestine.

The new juices and the intestine's own secretions are alkaline—they neutralize the acid—and their enzymes then act on the food to break it down even further. Cellulose and some fats resist but the rest of the food is now almost ready to yield its nutrients.

PAY $ TOLL

Pay lymph toll for ride to bloodstream.

Leftover fats wait to be picked up by lymph for storage; fatty acids and glycerol proceed to liver.

TO WAIT

Submit to massage from intestinal wall and villi.

Small, usable particles of food wait here for free ride in bloodstream to liver. Others proceed to 10.

ADMIT ONE

FREE RIDE

USABLE

Water, wait here to be absorbed.

Food particles still unabsorbed, go directly to 12.

Pay here for bacterial decay and proceed to 13.

12

Proceed through colon.

13

Finish.

Take another turn in caecum; for penalty, wait out one turn.

WAIT

11

GO

Food particles still not usable; proceed to 11.

The Digestive System

The Intestinal Roller-Coaster Ride

Having been chewed, churned and bathed in digestive juices, food is now sent on a wild four- to eight-hour journey through the small intestine. Waves called peristalsis contort the intestine and swish the food solution back and forth. Millions of nearly microscopic fingers, or villi, projecting from the lining of the intestine stir the solution and transfer most usable nutrients into the blood and lymph systems.

What remains of the food solution spends 10 to 12 hours in the large intestine, losing large quantities of water and some more nutrients. As a final step, the solution is fed on by a colony of bacteria to decay the remains of what started out as a meal.

6

The Vital Pairs:
The Lungs
and Kidneys

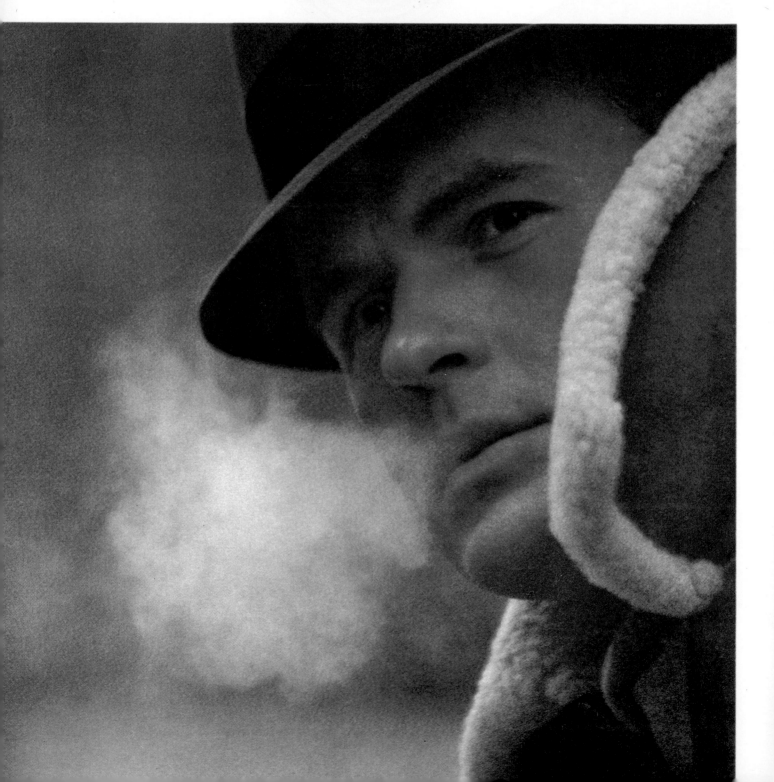

WHEN JOHN DONNE WROTE THAT "No man is an island, entire of itself," he was referring to the mind and the spirit of man. His classic phrase, however, can be applied to the body of man as well. For no human body can flourish independent of the world beyond its own skin. Like a medieval castle, it has its fortifications and protective moats. Yet it is far from self-sustaining. From the surrounding environment it must obtain food, water and oxygen; it must send back out the wastes which would otherwise poison it. To ensure this essential passage both ways, it must have its means of entry and exit.

The body has three main gateways: the digestive tract, discussed in the previous chapter; the lungs, through which we take in oxygen and breathe out carbon dioxide; and the kidneys, through which we excrete wastes in the form of urine. Unlike the drawbridges of the medieval castle, these gateways do not stand at the body's outermost ramparts; nevertheless, they mark the boundaries between its inside and outside. This seeming paradox has its roots in a popular misconception. To the layman, a cinder in his eye, a splinter embedded under his nail, the morsel of food which he has just popped into his mouth, are all unarguably "inside" his body. To the physiologist, however, they are really only on its outskirts. He considers food to be inside the body only after it has been digested and absorbed through the intestinal lining; oxygen only after it has been absorbed through the lung membrane. He considers water and waste materials to be outside the body immediately after they have been filtered out of the kidneys into the bladder.

Among the wonders of construction with which the body has been endowed, both the lungs and kidneys rank high on the list. As if in token of the crucial nature of their allotted tasks, each is a paired organ. Many a human being is alive and thriving today, despite damage or actual removal of one lung or kidney, because the remaining organ fills the breach and continues to do the work of both.

This is but one indication, however, of the importance to the body of the proper functioning of its respiratory and excretory systems. The body's trillions of cells require so much oxygen that we need about 30 times as much surface for its intake as our entire skin area covers. The lungs provide this surface area—even though they weigh only about two and a half pounds, and fit neatly within the chest cavity—by virtue of the fact that their membranes fold over and over on themselves in pockets so thin that a sheet of the finest paper seems grossly thick by comparison. The kidneys, each no more than four or five inches long, are no less astonishingly equipped to cope with their particular duties. An estimated 42 gallons of water—about twice the body's entire weight in fluid—filter down the kidney tubules every day. This flood is dealt with by millions of tiny mechanisms called nephrons, working in shifts

THE BREATH OF LIFE
The functioning of the lungs is most readily apparent in winter, when the cold quickly condenses moisture-laden puffs of exhaled air into miniature clouds. In their crucial capacity as a medium of exchange, the lungs sustain life by unloading carbon dioxide and taking in oxygen. Carried by the blood to the cells, oxygen unlocks the energy contained in the body's fuels.

and selectively reabsorbing most of the fluid back into the bloodstream.

Selectivity, indeed, is the key to the activities of both kidneys and lungs. It is brought into play from the very instant that we take a breath of air. This holds true whether we are inhaling the stagnant air of a crowded cocktail party or the salt sea breeze on a lonely beach, for despite the forebodings of fresh-air fiends, the lungs handle both kinds with equal efficiency.

Even the purest country air contains dust particles and bacteria; city air, of course, is additionally burdened with soot and exhaust fumes. Whatever its content, the air, in the few brief seconds it takes to travel from the environment to the lungs, must pass muster by a preliminary board of review: the nose; the trachea, or windpipe; the bronchi—two large tubes, one for each lung—into which the windpipe divides behind the breastbone; and finally, issuing from the main bronchi, the smaller bronchi and tiny bronchioles—much like branches and twigs stemming from a tree trunk.

As it moves into these channels, the air attracts vigilant attention. In the nose, some of its dust particles and bacteria drop off simply because they cannot make their way through the twisting nasal passages; others are trapped either by mucus or by tiny hairs, cilia, that beat in a direction opposite to the incoming air flow. In the windpipe, most of the remaining bacteria in the air are intercepted by mucus; so are particles that have managed to get past the nose. When sufficiently irritating, the impurities accumulated in the nose and the particles in the windpipe respectively produce the explosive irritations we know as the sneeze and the cough.

Two studies in pink

Once beyond the nose and windpipe, the incoming air has received most of the screening it is going to get. The bronchi and bronchioles serve primarily as conduits direct to the lungs. The air they finally bring to the lungs has been cleansed as much as the valiant efforts of the preliminary channels—and the nature of the particular breather's environment—will permit. How heavily environmental factors figure may be seen in the contrast between an infant's lungs and those of an adult city-dweller with the smoking habit. The infant's lungs are a bright, healthy pink; the adult's, a dull pink-and-gray, mottled with black.

Arriving at the bronchioles, the air has yet to unload its cargo of oxygen. The start of this task is taken on by vast armies of tiny, expansible, thin-walled, clustering sacs called alveoli, in which the bronchioles terminate. The alveoli constitute the bulk of lung tissue; it is their substance which makes the lungs soft and spongy, and indeed so light that they can float. The lungs of an average-sized man contain an estimated 300 million of these air sacs. When the lungs expand or contract—on stimulus from a respiratory center in the brain—it is in fact the alveoli that are expanding or contracting. Their expansion provides the vital surface required for oxygen intake into the blood; the area covered by the membrane of the alveolar cells, in total, is some 600 square feet —enough for the floor area of a handsomely commodious living room.

A fateful film of moisture

The membrane of the alveoli is moist—another crucial factor. Oxygen, in its original gaseous state, cannot diffuse in the bloodstream; it must first be dissolved. The film of moisture coating the alveolar membrane effects this transformation. The evolution of this delicate apparatus deep within the body of man was, indeed, responsible for his ability to live exclusively on land. Amphibian animals, such as frogs, breathe directly through their skins as well as through their lungs. Had the human animal not developed a breathing membrane that stayed moist of itself, he might have had to face the somewhat impractical prospect of keeping his skin permanently wet in order to breathe at all.

Still another superlative bit of engineering helps effect the final entry of oxygen into the bloodstream. Into each lung a pulmonary artery carries a surge of blood directly from the heart, seeking fresh oxygen. In the lung, each of these arteries divides and subdivides into smaller and smaller vessels, dogging the paths of the small bronchi and bronchioles. Where the tiniest bronchioles terminate in the clusters of alveoli, the pulmonary vessels open out into a rich network of capillaries which surround each cluster like faithful shadows. Layers of capillary and alveolar cells thus lie in direct contact side by side—a double membrane, almost unimaginably thin, with air moving on one side and blood flowing past on the other.

Soaked into the blood via this virtually transparent wall, the oxygen molecules are snatched up by the hemoglobin in the blood. They cannot escape back into the lungs; as mentioned in Chapter 4, the iron in the hemoglobin locks the oxygen in a chemical embrace. Swept along in the bloodstream, the oxygen finally arrives at the body's waiting cells, there to unite with the body's fuels and free the energy in them.

The actual quantity of oxygen taken in during this process may vary from one minute to another, depending on the rate of breathing and the speed with which blood is being pumped through the arteries. This, in turn, depends on how much energy the body requires at the time. A man snoozing in a hammock may absorb only half a pint of oxygen a minute. A miler trying to beat a world's record may soak up more than five quarts in the same period.

The lungs do not rest on their laurels with the delivery of oxygen to

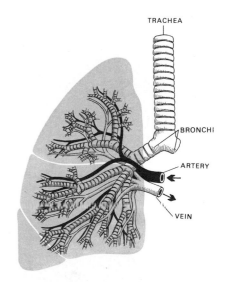

A CLOSE LOOK AT A LUNG

Air pulled down the trachea into the bronchi and lungs enters a network of millions of moist air sacs capable of expanding and contracting. Blood enters the lung via an artery and flows around the sacs in capillaries, giving up carbon dioxide and taking on oxygen. It then flows through a vein to the heart. The right lung, shown here, has three lobes; the smaller left lung has only two, making room for the heart.

121

the bloodstream. Simultaneously, they draw out of it the waste carbon dioxide which results from the combustion of carbon compounds in the cells. Picked up from these cells and carried along by the blood on its way to pick up oxygen from the lungs, the carbon dioxide is brought alongside the alveolar membrane, and seeps out from the bloodstream just as the oxygen seeps in. Although the two gases pass through the same membrane, they have absolutely nothing to do with each other. They are like total strangers boarding and leaving a train at a single signal. From the lungs, the carbon dioxide makes its way out of the body along the same route which the oxygen followed on its way in.

While an excess of carbon dioxide would be poisonous to the body, its complete removal would be fatal. A small amount is retained in the blood, and that amount is vital to life, as one of the great regulators of the chemistry of the body. It not only maintains the proper degree of acidity in body fluid but also controls the internal breathing mechanism.

A case of Jekyll and Hyde

The Jekyll-Hyde nature of carbon dioxide was confirmed only in recent decades. Its existence in the air was discovered as far back as the 17th Century by the Belgian scientist, Johann Baptista van Helmont. Its presence in the body, as a by-product of respiration, was discovered a century later by a Scottish chemist, Joseph Black. Not surprisingly, Black assumed that carbon dioxide was simply a waste. Then, in 1885, a German physiologist, Johann Friedrich Miescher-Rüsch, suggested that carbon dioxide actually played a major role in regulating how hard and fast we breathe. Twenty years later, two British physiologists, John Scott Haldane and an associate, J. G. Priestley, confirmed this assumption.

Haldane was one of those colorful individualists whose nonconformist behavior adds spice to the sedate annals of scientific research. One of his habits was to carry a watch which lacked a minute hand, ticking only the hours away; nevertheless he used it to keep appointments and was said never to have missed a train. He also indulged in the far greater gamble of experimenting on himself. When he began his investigations of the breathing process, it was common knowledge that people who become excited and breathe too quickly often suffer numbness, and sometimes even an uncontrollable twitching. These unpleasant sensations had generally been attributed to "oxygen poisoning," but Haldane thought they were more likely to be caused by the exhalation of too much carbon dioxide.

According to a popular medical school legend, one of the ways Haldane tested his theory was to sit on a stool in a steaming shower and pant furiously for several minutes. Soon he began to feel the expected symptoms. But by the time he was sure his theory was right—the story

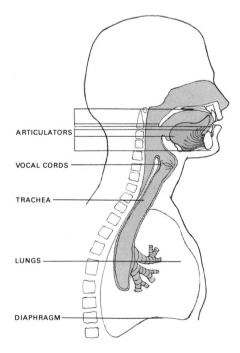

THE THEATER OF SOUND

Speech is produced by many muscular movements employing all of the body's orchestral parts, shown above. A sound begins when the lungs drive a current of air upward through the trachea and set the vocal cords vibrating in the larynx. The sound is now shaped in the air passage *(gray)* by movements of the articulators *(right)*—teeth, palate, lips, jaws and tongue—into the various vowel and consonant sounds of speech.

goes—his muscles were cramping so uncontrollably that he could neither turn off the shower nor get out of the shower room. Luckily an assistant happened by to rescue him.

Haldane always denied this story. In any case, in other experiments in closed respiration chambers, and under varying conditions of atmospheric pressure, he and Priestley demonstrated that carbon dioxide regulates the breathing through its effect on the respiratory center in the brain. To a certain very limited extent, we ourselves can decide to breathe lightly or deeply, slowly or quickly; in this sense we can control our respiration. But when such decisions bring the breather close to the danger point, the involuntary-control system takes over. After a few minutes of holding his breath, for example, a person is forced to inhale quickly and deeply. He does so, Haldane and Priestley proved, because carbon dioxide accumulates in his blood and stimulates the respiratory center to dictate renewed breathing.

Under normal conditions, the respiratory system works so smoothly that we are not even aware of it. It can, however, be interfered with in a number of ways: by the diversion of a piece of food into the windpipe, by certain ailments and by the inhalation of certain chemical fumes.

The illnesses which can affect the respiratory system are considerable in number. The common cold obstructs breathing by causing watery mucus to collect in the nose and block the flow of incoming air. The even more troublesome inflammation known as bronchitis obstructs the air flow by causing the lining of the air tubes to swell. Asthma, often brought on by allergy, anxiety or tension, can make muscles in the bronchi contract so that the victim continuously wheezes and gasps for air. The worst damage occurs when the alveoli are damaged or blocked so that oxygen cannot seep through them into the bloodstream. Such damage can be wrought by tuberculosis bacilli, which can destroy lung tissue, or by pneumonia, the lung inflammation which fills the alveoli with a sticky substance that keeps air from penetrating the membrane leading to the blood. This pair of diseases—the two worst killers in the United States in 1900—has been checked by the development of antibiotic drugs, but both are still dangerous.

Finality in a capsule

In addition to the obstruction of the air pipes and damage to the lung membrane, another means by which the body can be robbed of oxygen is through the intake of certain poisons. Hermann Goering, the second-ranking man in the Nazi hierarchy, cheated the executioner after the Nuremberg war-crimes trials in 1946 by swallowing a capsule of potassium cyanide, a chemical which prevents the proper use of oxygen by the cells. Another killer is carbon monoxide, inhaled from a defective stove or automobile exhaust pipe. Carbon monoxide, unlike carbon dioxide, has no redeeming features whatever. It cannot be usefully employed by the body. But by a fluke of nature, it attaches itself even more readily than oxygen to the hemoglobin in the blood. By doing so, it crowds out the oxygen, much as a cowbird hatched in another bird's nest will hog so much of the food that the legitimate nestlings starve.

Whatever its cause, anoxia—the cutting off of oxygen from the cells—will result in quick death. As Haldane himself expressed it, it not only brings about "the stoppage of a machine, it is also the total ruin of the supposed machinery."

The traffic passing through the gateway of the lungs is no more critical, however, than the traffic passing through the gateway of the kidneys. Besides carbon dioxide, the cells of the body cast off a host of unwanted substances, including nitrogen compounds, sulphates and phosphates. These remnants may be compared to the ashes left after a fire has burned all the coal it can. They, too, must be removed if the cellular furnaces are to function effectively, and their removal is the task of the kidneys.

These dark red organs, with their familiar bean shape, are situated not in the small of the back, as most people believe, but higher up, just behind the stomach and liver. They are, except for the brain, perhaps the most complex organs in the body. Ridding the body of wastes is only one of their jobs. They also regulate the chemical makeup of the blood and preserve the correct balance between salt and water in the body.

A miracle of ingenuity

The method by which the kidneys clean the wastes out of the bloodstream, where the cells have dumped them, is a miracle of ingenuity. When the blood flows into the kidneys, it is immediately channeled into clusters of capillaries. Each cluster, so small that the eye can barely see it, is called a glomerulus, from the Latin for "small ball." It is tightly enclosed by a double membrane which leads into a tubule, or little tube. The glomerulus, the membrane and the tubule together make up a single, highly intricate mechanism called a nephron. There are about two and a half million nephrons and, if all their tubules were straightened out, they would stretch for approximately 50 miles.

The kidneys do not simply pick waste products out of the bloodstream and send them along for final disposal. As blood courses through the glomeruli, much of its fluid, containing both useful chemicals and dissolved waste materials, soaks out through the membranes, much as carbon dioxide soaks into the lungs. Once through the membranes, it flows on into the tubules. The tubules proceed to send back into the bloodstream what is valuable and re-usable, leaving the waste products neatly trapped outside. This recapture of needed materials is carried

KIDNEY

URETER

BLADDER

URETHRA

CLEANSERS OF THE BODY'S FLUIDS

The two kidneys, with their ability to excrete unwanted materials and retain others, are the body's chief organs for cleansing its internal fluids. The kidneys are equipped with filtering, absorbing and secreting units called nephrons, shown much enlarged *(arrow)* at left and in detail opposite. Ureters carry the resulting urine to the bladder for temporary storage. Finally, the urine is discharged through the urethra.

out by chemical action. As the tubules twist and wind away from the glomeruli, they come back into contact with other capillaries. Here the valuable sugars and salt which have soaked into the tubules are seized by enzymes and yanked back into the bloodstream. At the same time, molecules of water are being forced back under pressure. The body cannot afford to lose the estimated 42 gallons of water that daily soak into the tubules in order to dissolve the departing wastes; therefore, most of it must be drawn back. Altogether, about 99 per cent of the fluid which filters out of the glomeruli is reabsorbed into the bloodstream. As it flows on down the tubules, the remaining 1 per cent, along with the wastes, is converted into urine. This drops into two other channels —the ureters—and then into the bladder to await expulsion.

The telltale trail of sugar

Even when the kidneys are operating at peak efficiency, the nephrons can reabsorb only so much sugar and water. Their limitations are dramatically illustrated in cases of *diabetes mellitus,* a disease which causes the amount of sugar in the blood to rise far above normal. Ordinarily, all the glucose that seeps out through the glomeruli into the tubules is reabsorbed into the blood. But if too much is present, the tubules reach the limit of their ability to pass the sugar back into the bloodstream, and retain some of it. It is then carried along in the urine, often providing a doctor with his first clue that a patient has *diabetes mellitus.* Indeed, the value of urine as a diagnostic aid has been known to the world of medicine as far back as the time of Hippocrates. From then on, examination of the urine became a regular procedure for physicians, and by the Middle Ages its study achieved the status of a science, uroscopy. For more than 500 years the standard work on the subject was *Carmina de Urinarum* ("A Poem of Urine") by Gilles de Corbeil, a French physician, written, after the fashion of his time, entirely in verse.

Because of the abiding importance of both the kidneys and the lungs to the maintenance of life, great effort has been expended to find substitute devices which can take over when either of these organs even partially fails beyond repair. One of the most notable successes along this line has been scored at the Artificial Kidney Center of the Swedish Hospital in Seattle, where patients with chronic kidney trouble may avail themselves, on a regular weekly basis, of a mechanical kidney substitute which filters wastes from the bloodstream. Medical scientists have also devoted serious study to the prospect that someday it may be possible to patch up an injured kidney with a cluster of kidney cells grown in a test tube from a tissue culture, and to replace a cancerous lung with a secondhand lung deep-frozen in an organ bank and thawed by microwave.

Both lungs and kidneys have garnered a large share of attention in the

GLOMERULUS

TUBULE

CAPILLARIES

COLLECTING TUBULE

TO MAIN BLOODSTREAM

FROM MAIN BLOODSTREAM

THE WORK OF THE NEPHRONS

The process of forming urine begins when arterial blood flows into a tuft of capillaries (the glomerulus) in the nephron, which filters out some of its fluid—not all of it waste. The fluid enters the tubule of the nephron, where useful sugars, salts and water are reabsorbed by capillaries and returned to the main bloodstream. The capillaries in turn secrete ammonia through the tubule wall into the fluid. The resulting waste is urine.

125

increasingly widespread effort to effect transplantations of internal organs. Thus far the kidney has proved the easiest of all organs to transplant, primarily because the surgical connection involved is the easiest. By the end of 1963 more than 300 kidney transplantations were known to have been performed around the world. Except for the few effected between identical twins, these efforts have been no more than temporarily successful. The problem persists of finding a way to override the body's natural tendency to reject strange intrusions.

Hope is seen, however, in the fact that more recent transplants have kept their recipients alive longer than earlier transplants were able to do. A New Orleans dockworker, operated on in late 1963 at the Tulane University School of Medicine, lived for two months on kidneys grafted into him from an 80-pound chimpanzee. Meanwhile, research goes on apace into the problem of countering the body's immunological forces. Of several approaches, the most promising thus far is the use of drugs to suppress the immunity system until the host body is "reconciled" with the guest organ. One enormous difficulty, however, is that this treatment also destroys the patient's defenses against infection. But even this seemingly insurmountable obstacle, it is believed, will be overcome in time. On this score, as on all the other life or death matters with which he deals, the medical scientist remains an incurable optimist.

Replacements for the Body's Faulty Parts

Ever since Hindu surgeons, about 800 B.C., used flaps of forehead skin to repair an amputated nose, doctors have dreamed of replacing diseased organs with tissue from a healthy donor. Every imaginable kind of transplantation has been tried, on animals (opposite) and on humans. Yet, with rare exceptions, tissue transplanted from one human being or species to another is doomed to die. Each individual is genetically unique, right down to his cells and proteins. Thus, when tissue is transplanted, it is regarded by the host as antigenic—that is, as an alien substance. It is rejected by means of the host's antibody-producing cells, the weapons it also uses against bacteria, which damage the alien cells of the graft. Undaunted, scientists are hunting for ways to make a body accept donated kidneys, lungs or other organs. This search, and the concurrent development of ingenious mechanical substitutes for organs, are depicted on the following pages.

INCOMPATIBLE RABBITS
The two white rabbits shown opposite, of different breeds, are rejecting skin grafts exchanged between them. The left ear of each bears a patch of skin taken from the other rabbit, and held in place with stitches. The transplanted tissue, which appears dark and scablike in the photograph, dies off because the host's built-in defenses destroy cells that are genetically different from its own.

MECHANICAL LEASE ON LIFE

The artificial kidney above removes the toxic waste products from a patient's five to six quarts of blood in about six hours, during which time the blood is pumped through the machine 14 times. A patient whose own kidneys are not functioning must spend two nights a week attached to this device by plastic tubes, worn permanently on the arm, shown opposite *(bottom)*.

BLOOD FROM ARTERY

BLOOD TO VEIN

OXYGEN CONTROL

COILED TUBING

PUMP

FILTER

RINSING FLUID

RINSING OUT THE WASTES

This diagram shows how the artificial kidney functions. Blood tapped from an artery in the forearm is drawn into a small electrical pump and sent through two cellulose tubes with micro-thin walls. The tubes are coiled in the core of the machine and bathed in an oxygenated solution similar to the body's plasma. As blood flows through the coils of the "kidney," small molecules of toxic wastes pass by osmosis into the bath. The cleansed blood, filtered to remove any bubbles, then re-enters a forearm vein.

The Medical Washing Machine

Until transplanted tissue can be used to replace diseased organs, some patients can be kept alive by artificial spare parts. Mechanical substitutes are particularly effective for the kidney function of filtering wastes from the blood. When both kidneys fail, either temporarily or permanently, the blood is soon poisoned with nitrogenous wastes, a condition called uremia. About 10,000 people die each year of uremia whose lives might have been saved either by a successful transplant or a machine. At present there are only some 500 artificial kidney machines in the U.S., caring for temporary failures and a tiny percentage of permanent failures—the latter at a cost of up to $10,000 a year per patient. For the permanently stricken, machines are a makeshift and expensive substitute for the transplant that is still impossible in most cases.

THE PORTABLE KIDNEY
A major advance would be the development of an internal artificial kidney that patients could operate at home. One such device, used successfully on a dog *(above)*, is a coil of cellophane tubing embedded in the abdomen (and visible in the X-ray picture). By means of tubes in the dog's skin, the device is hooked up to a portable machine that pumps cleansing fluid in and out.

OUTLET IN THE BLOODSTREAM
Long-term treatment with an artificial kidney machine is made possible by the horseshoe-shaped tubing, or shunt, worn in a patient's arm *(left)*. Without the shunt, blood vessels would have to be surgically opened for each treatment. When closed, the shunt links an artery and vein. During treatments it is opened and the two ends are hooked up to the machine.

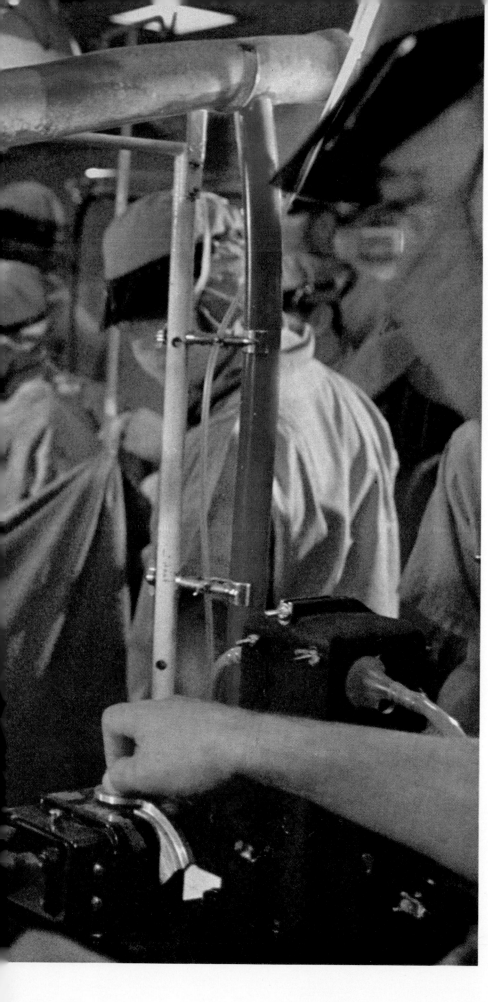

A "Bubble Bath" for the Blood

One of the most ingenious additions to the modern operating room is the machine at left, which can perform the functions of both the heart and lungs. Blood is siphoned off into the machine, bypassing those vital organs but continuing to circulate through the body—permitting surgical procedures on the heart that take up to three hours. Carbon dioxide is removed from the blood and oxygen added—normally done in the lungs—in a bubble chamber. The blood is then defoamed to remove all bubbles —leftover bubbles could be fatal— and piped back into the aorta. A small electric pump provides a "heartbeat."

Medical engineers are now at work developing mechanical hearts and lungs small enough to plant inside the body where they could permanently replace worn-out organs. They are trying to miniaturize a plastic membrane device that could replace a damaged lung, and have placed artificial hearts powered by electromagnets in calves with some success. The first such heart might be ready for a human within a few years.

Even now surgeons are replacing diseased heart valves with artificial ones, repairing damaged arteries or veins with lengths of plastic, and implanting a small electrical device that is able to spark a faltering heart.

REROUTING THE BLOODSTREAM
The patient is hidden behind a team of technicians and heart surgeons as his blood is pumped through a heart-lung machine. Rising through the bubble chamber at right, the blood changes color from dark (which indicates insufficient oxygen) to bright red (indicating oxygenation). The bubbles are then removed from the blood in the transverse tube at top and the helix at left.

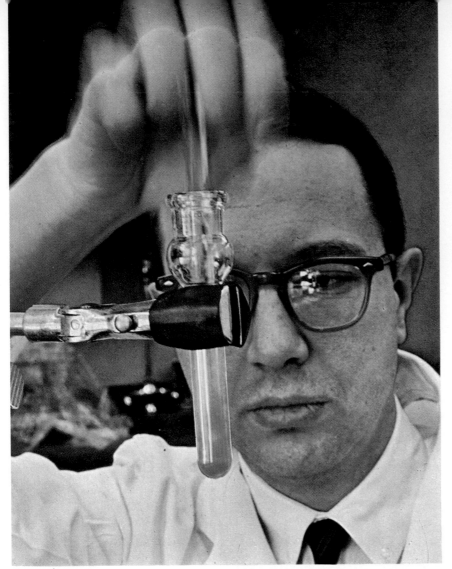

The Mixed Blessing of Immunity

The best machines are only makeshift substitutes for living tissue, and surgeons would much prefer to transplant a live organ than an artificial one. Before this becomes practical, however, much more research must be done on the reaction between the graft's antigens and the host's antibodies, the "immune reaction" by which the body can reject foreign tissue. It is probable that antigens are simply the normal, characteristic proteins of the transplanted cells. These are considered antigens only when placed in an alien environment. The host's antibodies, however, are large, unique proteins tailored to match specific antigens *(opposite)*. They are made to order by the protein builders of small lymph cells. The lymph cells invade the graft tissue, antibodies attack, and the tissue is deformed and damaged. It is ironic that this mechanism, evolved to provide immunity to disease, also destroys a grafted organ that could make the difference between life and death.

CLUES IN A TEST TUBE
The scientist above is breaking human lymph cells in a test tube to extract ribosomes, or protein-builders. The aim is to discover how the cells match protein antibodies to antigens. Experiments of this sort are offering clues as to the exact nature of the body's immune reaction.

A THIN SLICE OF LIFE
The microphotograph at right shows a thin slice of newly transplanted kidney tissue. The three large open areas are glomeruli, the kidney's capillaries for filtering the wastes from blood. The many small bodies are tubules through which concentrated urine is drained off the bladder.

A PICTURE OF DEATH
Rejection of the kidney is seen in the microphotograph at right. The tubules are no longer intact. A scarred arteriole *(center)* is surrounded by the host's invading lymph cells, whose antibodies have locked onto the graft's antigens. The attack soon causes the graft to degenerate.

132

DETECTING CELL

NUCLEUS

GENETIC CODE   ALTERED CODE

(A)

BODY'S OWN
PROTEIN

ANTIGEN

ANTIBODY PRODUCING CELLS

ALTERED CODE

TEMPLATE

(B)

ANTIBODIES

(C)

LAUNCHING AN ATTACK ON FOREIGN TISSUE

The schematic diagram above depicts one hypothesis of how the immune reaction works. An antigen *(red)* from grafted tissue enters an antigen-detecting cell *(left)* in the lymph nodes. This cell is coded, perhaps with a genetically determined chain of unique structure *(gray),* to match the body's own proteins *(blue).* The new antigen does not match, and the detecting cell must alter some of this code to conform to the new antigen (A). This altered code is passed to an antibody-producing cell *(center),* which in turn molds images, or "templates," of the new antigen (B). The templates serve as dies against which antibodies can be cast—the process shown in the third panel, at right. The antibodies are then released to lock onto and neutralize antigens en masse (C). In the diagram below, the host's lymph cells are shown swarming to the graft, where they release antibodies to block acceptance of the graft tissue.

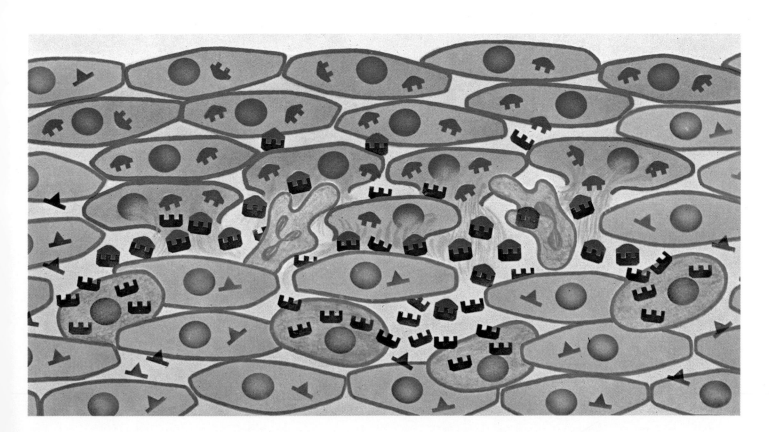

Operating against All Odds

Despite the present odds against success, more than 300 kidney transplants have been made since the first attempt in 1954. Yet less than 5 per cent of these have lasted more than a year. Unless taken from an identical twin, whose proteins are genetically the same, the graft tissue is soon attacked by the host's antibody-producing lymph cells and is rejected.

A kidney is the organ most often transplanted because a donor can function on the remaining one of his pair. But it is technically possible to transplant virtually any organ from one person to another. Indeed, surgeons have recently taken lungs and hearts from fresh cadavers or even animals in desperate efforts to save a patient's life. In early 1964, for instance, a chimpanzee's heart was grafted to a human. Such measures are a last resort. When there is no hope of restoring the heart of the patient on the operating table, the surgeon must signal to a technician at the artificial heart-lung machine to turn it off. As one heart surgeon explains, "When the technician switches off that little knob, the patient has a life expectancy of five minutes." The patient with the chimpanzee heart died. But even a hopeless graft may seem preferable to that fatal nod.

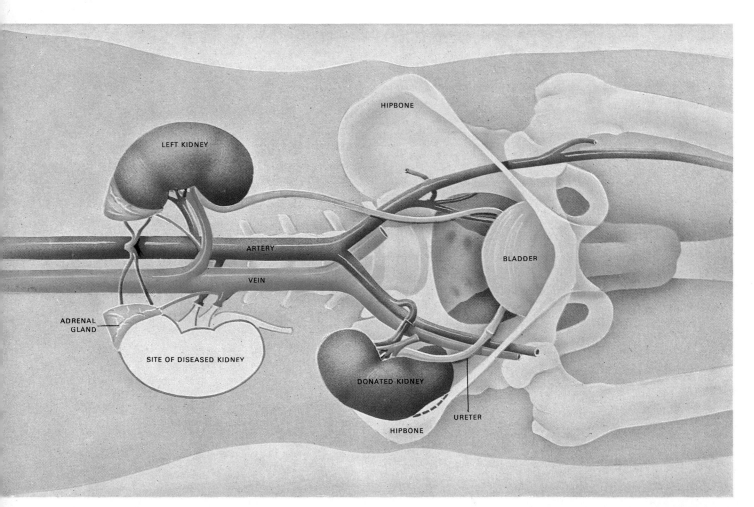

BLUEPRINT FOR A TRANSPLANT
In making a kidney transplant *(above diagram)*, surgeons remove only one of the patient's diseased kidneys, leaving the adrenal gland intact, and embed the donated kidney against the hipbone—an unnatural site chosen for surgical convenience. Sections of ureter, artery and vein come with the transplanted organ and must be sutured to the host's ureter and blood vessels.

HANGING BY A THREAD
A surgeon holds a donor's kidney in a cloth sling *(opposite)*, preparing to lower it through an incision in the patient's side. Moments before, a second team of surgeons removed the donated organ in an adjoining operating room, placed it in an iced bath and rushed it to the host for transplantation. The whole operation, from incision to sutures, takes about four hours.

Outwitting the Antibodies

After making a surgically successful transplant, surgeons must turn to the arts of immunological persuasion. The trick is to force the graft on a potentially resistant host by putting the host's defenses out of order. Two effective techniques for suppressing the immune reaction are X-ray treatment and the use of drugs.

Sledge-hammer doses of X-rays covering the entire body *(opposite)* destroy the lymph cells that produce antibodies. But this drastic treatment also wipes out the body's ability to fight off any infection, and a patient must remain in a sterile room for three to four weeks, until his body is producing lymph cells again, for the slightest infection could prove fatal. Indeed, some irradiated patients have been ravaged by the ordinarily benign bacteria of their own intestinal tract. Radiologists have lately refined their technique, aiming the X-rays solely at the major centers of lymph tissue and the transplantation site.

A safer and more effective technique, discovered as a by-product of cancer research, is the use of drugs *(below)* which seems to suppress immune reactions. "Immuno-suppressive" drugs, administered along with the graft, seem to decrease the production of new antibodies directed against antigens at least temporarily —but permit the body to retain its already-existing defenses against infection. Periodically, however, the body may renew its production of antibodies for fresh attacks on the graft. The best that medical science can do during such crises is to use a mixed bag of drugs, sometimes in concert with radiation, to keep the graft safe and sound. No sure way is yet known to persuade the host to accept foreign tissue permanently.

HEAD-TO-TOE IRRADIATION
Curled up so that his whole body receives a massive dose of X-rays, a patient at Boston's Peter Bent Brigham Hospital is being prepared for a kidney transplant from a non-identical twin. Five years after this history-making operation the patient was still alive, taking regular doses of an antibody-inhibiting drug and returning to the hospital for yearly examinations.

DIET OF PILLS
The graft recipient *(right)* may have to consume a massive number of pills to keep his body from rejecting the graft. The jars and pills (right foreground) are a six-month supply of immunity-suppressing pills taken daily. If production of antibodies begins anew, the patient may also be given the pills at left (up to 100 a week), experimental capsules *(center, rear)* and injections.

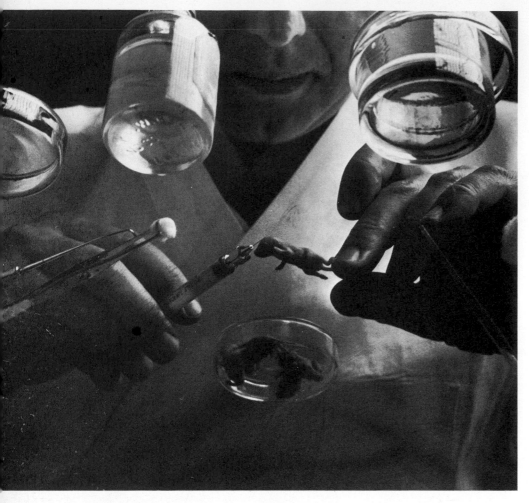

An Ounce of Prevention

Increased understanding of the immune mechanism may soon make tissue transplants common. For hard as it is to overcome an immune reaction, it now seems possible to induce life-long tolerance to foreign tissues by injecting antigens into a baby's blood —before the body learns to recognize tissues as its own or antigenic.

In the first days of life, the thymus gland *(opposite)* manufactures master lymph cells coded for all the body's own proteins. These master cells are distributed to the bone marrow, the lymph nodes and the spleen, which thereafter serve as seats of antibody production.

In recent experiments *(left)*, mice were injected with antigens before the thymus gland had coded the master lymph cells. These antigens were accepted as though they were the body's own proteins, and no antibodies were produced. Thus scientists speculate that, once the handful of basic human tissue types is identified, a human infant could receive an inoculation of mixed antigens that would make it more tolerant to later transplantations without making it more susceptible to disease. The immune reaction to a transplant might then be so slight that present drugs would suffice to make the grafted tissue take—and permanently survive.

MIXING MOUSE CELLS
Newborn mice of two strains are injected at birth with each other's characteristic antigens. In this case, lymph cells from the spleen are used as antigens. If this is done before the antibody-forming cells have been activated, the mouse can accept the antigens as a part of its own makeup, and later does not reject tissues that are grafted from the donor strain.

BROTHERS UNDER THE SKIN
The white mouse above has accepted a skin graft from a black mouse with which it exchanged spleen cells at birth. Immunologically, the two act like identical twins. In rare cases, twin human embryos, although not identical, share a single placenta, and the resulting interchange of their bloodstreams enables them to accept grafts from each other in later life.

IMMUNITY'S INCEPTION
At birth the thymus gland is larger than a baby's fist, as illustrated by the rubber model of the gland shown opposite. Located beneath the breastbone, the thymus early manufactures a master set of antigen-recognizing cells, then it slowly shrivels to about the size of a thumb.

7

A Network
That
Never Sleeps

A HORN BLARES, and a child stepping off a curb leaps back to safety as a truck he had not seen thunders past. A housewife slumbers undisturbed through the clamor of her neighbor's television set, but rouses to instant wakefulness at the first whimper from her baby in the adjoining room. A businessman wrestles for days with a problem that seems to defy solution—and then the answer comes to him out of the blue while he is busy thinking about something entirely different.

These are just three examples of the routine, everyday functioning of the human nervous system. Even a thousand examples would not suffice to describe its capabilities. Its presence in the body makes of each of us, in effect, a vast switchboard of humming, flashing, blinking signals, constantly sending and receiving messages—some urgent, some not, all concerned with the conduct of the body's affairs. From the moment we are born to the moment we die, this communications network controls our every thought, our every emotion, every step we take, every impression we get. Without it we could not plan, feel, move a muscle, nor distinguish between pleasure and pain; we would be deprived of such amenities of life as the enjoyment of food, or music, or the color of a painting, or the pressure of a friendly handshake.

The nervous system, operating by electrochemical impulses, serves the body in a variety of ways. It functions as the body's lookout; as gatherer of information about the world outside us as well as the one within us; as the clearinghouse where this information is processed for instant use or future reference; as general communications center; and as headquarters for mapping the strategy and making the decisions in everything the body does. The nervous system, in short, is the initiator of the body's muscular activity, and the regulator of our mental and physical functions.

This dynamic system of controls is composed of a tissue made up of nerve cells, or neurons, interspersed with other cells, called glia. The brain and the spinal cord serve as the system's main base of operations. From them a prodigious network of nerves reaches out to every part of the body.

For all its formidable role, the brain has an unprepossessing look. It is soft, gray, and furrowed, and about the size and shape of an acorn squash. All told, it weighs about three pounds. It has a four-inch-long, one-inch-wide central core, or brainstem, extending upward from the spinal cord. On either side of this core, and behind it, lies a mass of nervous tissue, the cerebellum. Draped over the brainstem and cerebellum is the cerebrum. Its outer layer, the cerebral cortex, is folded and convoluted to fit into the six-by-eight-inch vault of the skull; if flattened out, the cortex would cover more than two square feet in area. A fissure down the middle divides the cerebrum into two hemispheres connected

A MEMORABLE LEGACY
This forest of nerves, with its gleaming eyes, comprises part of the remains of a Philadelphia scrubwoman who willed her body to science some 75 years ago. Each nerve, painstakingly removed from the cadaver, was painted white for display. The area shown is but a fraction of the complex nervous system that rules all body activities, from wiggling toes to creating ideas.

by glistening bands, much lighter in color than the gray exterior tissue. Here, as elsewhere in the nervous system, the two colors represent a significant difference. The gray matter is made up of gray nerve-cell bodies. The white matter is made up of nerve fibers—axons—which extend from the cell bodies and are capable of conducting nerve impulses. What gives these fibers their color, as well as a generally waxy look, is a fatty coating, myelin, which not only insulates the fiber but also makes it a speedier conductor.

The spinal cord, which is about 18 inches long, resembles a cable tapered at both ends; at its widest, it is a little more than half an inch across. Like the brain, the spinal cord contains both gray and white matter; the gray nerve-cell bodies form a column in the center of the cord, sheathed by the white bundles of nerve fibers. Surrounding the cord on the outside is a perforated tunnel of bone formed by the rings of the vertebrae —the body's backbone.

A reach from tip to toe

The network of nerves which threads the body is rooted both in the brain and in the spinal cord. From the brain, nerve fibers converge to form 12 pairs of so-called cranial nerves serving the head, eyes, ears, throat, and some organs in the chest and abdomen. From the spinal cord 31 pairs of nerves pass out through openings between the vertebrae at various levels. From the upper part of the cord some of these nerves branch and rebranch to form nerve trunks leading to the upper torso, arms and hands. From the lower part of the cord other nerves branch and rebranch to form nerve trunks leading to the pelvis, thighs, legs and feet. The nerves reach every millimeter of skin surface, every muscle, every blood vessel, every bone—every part of the body from tip to toe. Each carries impulses—electrochemical signals—that are triggered by some stimulus.

The basic unit of the nervous system—the neuron—has one structural characteristic which distinguishes it from all other types of body cells. From the central part of the neuron thin fibers extend like delicate tendrils. Depending upon their location and function neurons may be anywhere from a fraction of an inch to as much as three or four feet long (the longest reaches from the base of the brain to the big toe). It is via their fibers that the neurons perform their unique function of transmitting signals to and from the brain and spinal cord. Upon receiving a signal, one neuron sends it on to another neuron lying adjacent to it across a kind of "spark gap" called a synapse. Thus the neurons form an entire chain, like a bucket brigade. From various parts of the body via the spinal cord or directly to the brain go signals which produce sensations of sight, sound, pain, pressure, touch, heat or cold. Back from the brain or the spinal cord

THE BACKBONE OF THE NERVOUS SYSTEM

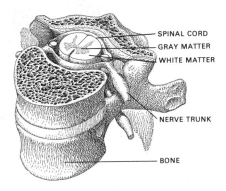

SPINAL CORD
GRAY MATTER
WHITE MATTER

NERVE TRUNK

BONE

A WELL-SHEATHED CABLE
From the lower vertebrae to the brain runs a communication cable that makes modern microcircuitry cumbersome in comparison. The spinal cord is wrapped in three layers of protective membranes, with fluid between two of the layers, and the whole encased in the heavy bone of the spine *(above),* making it almost impervious to injuries. Nerve impulses travel to and fro between it and the outer reaches of the body via 31 pairs of nerve trunks. The cord itself *(below)* is an elliptical column of white and gray matter. The white matter contains sensory nerves *(striped area)* leading to the brain and motor nerves *(dark area)* from the brain; the gray matter contains a gelatinous mass of connecting neurons.

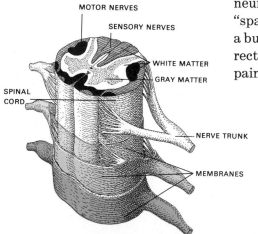

MOTOR NERVES

SENSORY NERVES

WHITE MATTER

GRAY MATTER

SPINAL CORD

NERVE TRUNK

MEMBRANES

go "orders"—motor signals—to muscles in the fingers, toes, heart, intestines and elsewhere.

There are three general classes of neurons, grouped according to their function. Sensory neurons carry signals to the spinal cord and brain. Motor neurons carry directives from the brain and spinal cord, both to stimulate the contraction or relaxation of muscles and to spur the activity of glands. Finally, connecting neurons—interneurons—shuttle the signals back and forth, through complex pathways, between the brain, spinal cord and other parts of the body. Interneurons comprise over 99 per cent of the more than 10 billion neurons in the nervous system, including most of the nerve cells of the brain itself.

The sensory neurons keep the brain informed of what is happening to and in the body through a wide variety of sensory pick-up units called receptors. Some of these, lying at or near the skin surface, are specially sensitive to pain, or touch, or pressure, or temperature (either hot or cold). Other receptors on the tongue and in the upper parts of the nose respond to flavors and odors. In the retina of the eye, special rodlike receptors respond to light and shadow of different intensities and wavelengths, while conelike receptors respond to color. Sensory receptors in the ear respond to minute vibrations caused by sound waves impinging on the eardrum. Other receptors are embedded deep in the digestive tract, in the walls of the intestines; when the intestines are confronted by indigestible food or by gas, these receptors transmit signals of pain, which are then interpreted as cramps. Still other receptors which are lodged in the muscles, ligaments or tendons fire off signals to the brain any time a muscle contracts or a joint moves or is subjected to added pressure and tension.

The sizzling steak stimulus

All the varied sensory stimuli picked up by the receptors must be converted into signals before they can be transmitted anywhere. In every case the signal is of the same kind—an electrochemical impulse. Depending on the type of stimulus, the conversion is set off in one of two ways. If the stimulus is mechanical—the touch of a pin on the skin, an impinging sound wave or a stretching of the intestinal wall—the nerve endings are, so to speak, pinched; this action initiates the impulse. If the stimulus is chemical—as when aromatic vapors from a sizzling steak encounter the smell receptors in the nose, or when light causes changes in the rods and cones of the retina—the chemical reaction alone triggers the impulse. In either event the impulse travels as a sort of electrochemical wave of activity, passing along the nerve at the rate of anywhere from one to 350 feet per second. The speed depends on the size and type of the particular nerve fiber and the thickness of the coating of myelin around it. Certain fibers which lack myelin are comparatively slow transmitters.

We tend to think of a nerve stimulus only in terms of warnings of danger—a stab of pain, for instance, or a flash of bright light, or a clanging bell. Actually, we receive sensory stimuli all the time, whether danger impends or not. During a deep sleep, for example, we would not continue breathing unless specially sensitive receptors in the circulatory system signaled the brain of an increase in the level of carbon dioxide in the blood. But there is no basic difference between the signals of stabbing pain from a pricked finger and the steady flow of unperceived impulses that maintain breathing. The major difference lies in where these impulses start, where they are brought to our consciousness (if they are), and where they take effect.

Each sensory receptor, furthermore, responds only to its own particular kind of stimulus. A pain receptor which is lying side by side with touch receptors will, under ordinary circumstances, single out only its own message. Occasionally, however, when stimuli are exceptionally strong, they can excite receptors that are not usually sensitive to them. Receptors in the retina, for example, normally respond only to visual stimuli. But sensations of flashing light can also be triggered by pressure on the eyeball.

Sensations in tandem

Several types of receptors acting in combination can produce more complex sensory experiences. We may find a particular food palatable or unpalatable, for example, not only because of how it tastes and smells, but also because of how it appeals to the eye. We may simultaneously experience sensations of touch, pressure, heat and pain in lifting a pot from the stove.

While the sensory neurons are bringing in information from all parts of the body to the brain, motor neurons are at the same time carrying directions from the brain to the muscles—signals which prod them into activity. The fibers of these neurons terminate in tiny flat plates—so-called "motor end plates"—which lie in close contact with individual muscle fibers. Here the nerve ending is separated from the muscle only by a tiny gap.

Even this minute space would stop motor signals in their tracks except for a special chemical reaction that takes place at the gap. As the impulse reaches the motor end plate, the nerve ending releases a chemical substance known as acetylcholine, which initiates events in the muscle cell. With the muscle's contraction, another substance—an enzyme called cholinesterase—begins breaking down the accumulated acetylcholine and clearing it away so that the next arriving nerve impulse can set the

SENSORY NERVE ENDINGS

NERVE FIBER

CELL BODY

SENSORY NEURON

TERMINALS

INTERNEURON

MUSCLE FIBERS

MOTOR NEURON

MOTOR NERVE ENDINGS

THE ROUTE OF A NERVE IMPULSE

Nerve impulses, from the reception of a stimulus to contraction of a muscle, are conveyed by neurons—each consisting of a cell body, nerve fiber, and fiber endings. A stimulus at the endings of a sensory neuron triggers impulses which race along the nerve fiber, through the cell body to terminals in the spinal cord. There an interneuron transmits the impulses to a motor neuron. The process ends in the muscle, which contracts as ordered.

144

cycle in motion again. It is this rechargeable chemical cycle that efficiently bridges the gap between motor nerve ending and muscle cell so that muscle action can be stimulated.

Determining which muscles contract and which relax in the continuous adjustments required to maintain our body's balance and keep us upright is a function of the lower-echelon centers of the brain—the brainstem and cerebellum. These also control our respiration and rate of heartbeat, and perform a multitude of other essential maintenance jobs. Somewhat higher echelons of the brain regulate body temperature, appetite, and such complex motor activities as walking, running and reaching for objects. The highest echelon of the brain—the cerebral cortex—gives us our awareness of sight and sound, as well as delicate sensations of weight, texture and form. It also initiates emotional responses such as hate, fear and anger, and enables us to experience pleasure or pain.

The site of sophistication

The cerebral cortex—the general staff of the nervous system, so to speak—exercises the most sophisticated form of control over incoming signals. It not only records signals and acts upon them, if necessary, but also interprets them or stores them for future reference. The cortex is thus responsible for decision-making and for the selection of the best course of action to follow at any given time. Its control centers are involved in all of our conscious intellectual functions, such as thinking, worrying, planning ahead or problem-solving.

A great deal about the activities of the brain is still imperfectly understood, and indeed it is only within the past decade or so that a plausible explanation has been found for one of the most baffling operations of the nervous system: the way in which an electrochemical impulse travels along a nerve fiber. In the early 1950s two Britishers, Alan Lloyd Hodgkin and Andrew Fielding Huxley, propounded an ingenious theory to explain the mechanism involved (some of the experiments involved were performed on the squid, whose giant nerve fibers are about 50 times as thick as mammalian nerve fibers and hence easier to work with). The work was later supplemented by an Australian, Sir John Carew Eccles. By 1963 such a wealth of evidence supported their ideas that all three were jointly awarded a Nobel Prize in medicine for their work.

In essence the theory holds that a nerve impulse, once started at the end of a nerve fiber, is kicked along by a series of electrical nudges. The process is so instantaneous that a single fiber can boost along up to 1,000 separate impulses in a single second, pausing after each has passed before handling the next. All this occurs as a result of a fleeting change in the cell membrane of the nerve fiber. Ordinarily the membrane serves as a

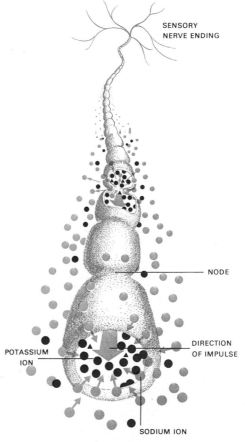

SENSORY
NERVE ENDING

NODE

DIRECTION
OF IMPULSE

POTASSIUM
ION

SODIUM ION

THE POWER PLANT OF NERVES
A nerve impulse is a self-perpetuating series of electrical charges along an insulated nerve fiber. The fiber, surrounded by positive sodium ions, has potassium ions in its negative interior. Whenever a sensory nerve ending is stimulated, the sodium is temporarily admitted into the nerve at a node—a break in the insulation. The resulting electrical charge sets off a chain of charges extending from node to node to the central nervous system.

145

barrier between two concentrations of electrically charged ions—potassium ions inside the nerve fiber and sodium ions in the body fluid outside it. But when a nerve impulse is set off—by a sound receptor in the ear, for example—the cell membrane briefly alters to allow charged potassium ions to flow out of the cell and charged sodium ions to flow in. This back-and-forth shuttling creates a tiny electrical potential, just strong enough to push the impulse a little farther along the fiber. Once the impulse has passed, the cell membrane resumes its role as barrier—until another impulse turns up.

A time for problem-solving

The complicated and busy nervous system consumes energy at an astounding rate. Nerve cells, therefore, require far more fuel—oxygen and glucose—than other cells; thus they must have a continuous and rich supply of blood or they will quickly die. Nerve cells in the brain alone use up as much as 20 per cent of all the oxygen available in the adult body, for they are working at frantic speed 24 hours a day. This may seem curious, since we think of sleep as "giving the brain a rest." But the brain is indisputably active during sleep periods. Quite aside from maintaining breathing and the rate of heartbeat, the brain may use these periods to try to search out answers to particularly difficult problems and to reconsider experiences of the day that were flowing in too fast to be dealt with carefully at the time.

By night or day, the brain's need for blood-borne oxygen never flags. Normally, during the course of every 24 hours, we lose some neurons simply because they wear out and die. Fortunately great numbers would have to die to produce any noticeable effect, but the small losses inevitably accumulate. Neurologists today believe that the insidious loss of mental efficiency that occurs in old age—the process we call senility—is a direct result of day-by-day destruction of a few neurons here and there, until the total loss begins to mount up and is accelerated by narrowing of blood vessels to the brain. Whatever the cause of the loss, once a neuron is destroyed it is destroyed. No new nerve cell will ever take its place; a year-old baby has all the neurons it will ever have. If only a nerve fiber is cut, and the cell itself is not killed, a new fiber may eventually grow out along the course of the cut fiber. But if the nucleus of the neuron is destroyed, the cell is gone forever. Such diseases as poliomyelitis cause paralysis because they destroy nerve nuclei which serve the muscle fibers, so that the muscles can never again receive directive impulses. The muscles atrophy, and the damage is permanent, even if the victim fights off the polio virus and survives.

Because the body could not tolerate the loss of too many neurons, and because nervous tissue is innately fragile, the nervous system operates behind an impressive wall of protection. The brain is encased in the tough armor plate of the skull. The spinal cord is enclosed in a strong but flexible bony sheath made up of the vertebrae. Both brain and spinal cord, furthermore, are surrounded by a clear cerebrospinal fluid which serves, among other purposes, as a shock absorber.

The rest of the nervous system is also well protected. The nerve trunks throughout the body are deeply buried between layers of muscle, except in such rare places as the point where the ulnar nerve crosses the elbow just beneath the skin—the easily shockable "funny bone." Many of the delicate receptor endings of sensory nerves are also carefully shielded. The nerve endings in the retina lie at the back of the eye, which is buried in a deep bony socket; they are protected from too much light by the self-adjusting shutterlike diaphragm of the iris. Sound receptors are encased deep within the ear in tiny bony caverns in the skull. Certain receptors—those sensitive to pain, touch, heat and cold, which lie at or near the surface of the skin—are relatively exposed. They are so widely distributed, however, that the loss of a few here and there is not important.

Under this massive cloak of protection, the nervous system conducts its complex activities with brilliant dispatch. Nerve impulses are transmitted so rapidly that a whole sequence of actions, interpretations and responses can take place before we are even aware that anything has happened. Indeed, a single stimulus may fire off thousands upon thousands of responses within a fraction of a second.

The nuances of a nicked finger

Consider, for example, the train of events that follows after we accidentally nick a finger with a knife while slicing bread. First, this injury stimulates a primitive protective reflex action—a kind of short circuit by which the pain signal from the finger triggers motor nerves in the spinal cord, instantaneously forcing us to jerk our hand back before word of the injury ever gets to the brain. But the pain stimulus is also picked up by interneurons in the spinal cord, so that news of the cut finger (and of the reflex response) is simultaneously "echoed" to the brain, setting off a chain reaction during the next few seconds.

Just how many individual signals fly to and from the brain during this reaction we can only guess; there may be tens of thousands. Here, in roughly chronological order, are but a few of the many signals and the ways in which we may deal with them:

Involuntary exclamation (set off by signals to speech areas of brain): Ouch!

Awareness (as cerebral cortex receives report of sudden movements): Something happened and I jerked my hand away from the breadboard.

THE VERTEBRATE BRAIN

The brains of all vertebrates—from the frog to man—have the same basic parts: the medulla controls such involuntary activities as respiration; the cerebellum maintains balance and posture; the thalamus acts as a message-relay center. The differences in brain power that we call intelligence are due to variations in the size and complexity of the cerebrum, the seat of reason. A frog, which operates mostly by reflex, or involuntary, actions, will be little changed if his cerebrum is removed. But deprive man of his cerebrum, and his ability to function will be completely destroyed. His cerebrum's crowning development is a convoluted casing of nervous tissue called the cerebral cortex; a biological rule of thumb seems to be: the more complex the cortex, the more intelligent the animal.

FROG

GOOSE

MONKEY

MAN

147

Heightened awareness (as other signals reach the cortex and are interpreted as pain): Whatever it was, it hurts.

Questions (generated by complex patterns of signals within cortex): What was it? Any damage done?

Purposeful response (as cortex sifts information): Lift up the finger and look at it.

Observation (as cortex processes data): It's bleeding; obviously it's cut.

Evaluation (in wake of data processing): Not too bad; just a nick.

Sensation of relief (also in wake of data processing): No need to worry.

Orders (unconscious): All right, heart, slow down. Adrenals, relax.

Orders (conscious): Okay, find some antiseptic and a bandage; wrap up the finger; get back to making the sandwiches.

Storage of data for future use: Item—check any knife for sharpness before you use it; item—that's what a nicked finger feels like; item—don't panic next time over a few drops of blood.

This silent soliloquy barely hints at the flurry of motor activity, information-gathering, evaluation and decision-making that a minor accident has set off. Many other reactions may be stirred up at the same time. How could I have been so careless? Any danger of infection? What happened to the coffee I left perking when I started to slice the bread? These and dozens more questions are passing through the mind, to say nothing of reactions such as self-annoyance at responding so excitedly to a superficial injury, frustration at not being able to hit back at the knife, relief that the cut didn't go any deeper, and so on. The really amazing aspect of this innocuous accident is the sheer volume of information that is sifted in its wake by the brain, and the remarkable speed with which the sifting occurs.

A panic-free pattern

A somewhat different chain reaction would occur if we were to take the knife and deliberately test the edge on our fingertip just to see how sharp it is. Again responses are triggered in the brain. But this time there is no involuntary spinal cord reflex unless we nick ourselves harder than we expected to. Such a reflex has already been blocked in advance. We may feel a sensation of pain, but there is no sudden alarm, no racing of the heart. Again, however, the brain busily stores information for future reference. The knife is definitely sharp. I can bear down on it only so much without drawing blood. I must remember to keep it out of reach of the children. These reactions are under voluntary control; there is less need for such an intricate sequence of perception, investigation, judgment, decision and physical action to unfold. Just as the nervous system can trigger these activities, it can also modify them to achieve a sensible, panic-free pattern of body behavior.

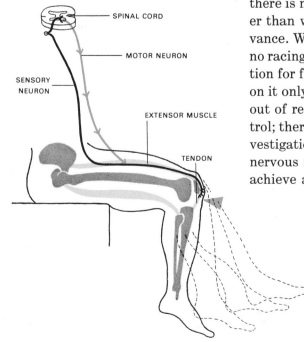

SPINAL CORD

MOTOR NEURON

SENSORY NEURON

EXTENSOR MUSCLE

TENDON

MECHANICS OF THE KNEE REFLEX

When a doctor taps a knee tendon, he activates one of the few two-neuron reflex arcs in the body. The blow stretches the extensor muscle, and a sensory neuron relays this information to the spinal cord. Here a motor neuron is automatically stimulated to counteract the stretch. But the motor neuron normally overcompensates, causing the extensor muscle to contract sharply and jerk the foot forward in an involuntary kick.

Taken as a whole, the nervous system provides an incredibly rich mass of information for the body about its internal and external environment. Indeed, recent experiments indicate that we depend strongly—perhaps for our very sanity—upon a constant flow of impressions from the outside world. Volunteers in such experiments, when deprived of these contacts for only a few hours—by being blindfolded, for instance, and suspended in a tank of warm, gently flowing water—quickly began to develop fantastic daydreams or even hallucinations. Some lost their sense of time; others heard singing choruses; others developed a confused sense of taste, mistaking the bologna they were fed for ham. For the most part, however, the hallucinations were visual. One man was convinced that he was seeing a herd of pink, blue, and purple elephants; another believed that he was seeing a hippopotamus come charging out of an instrument case; still another insisted that a small nearby shelf was crammed with grayish black socks.

The undetected sneaks

However, the impressions which we receive from the world around us are limited to those for which we have sensory receptors. Certain dangers can sneak undetected past this early warning system. Overexposure to the sun may lead to a disabling sunburn, yet the body has no notification of danger until the damage is already done, for we have no receptors that can detect the superabundance of ultraviolet light. Foreign proteins to which the body is sensitive can gain access to the bloodstream; we may have no hint of trouble unless special mechanisms built into our cells swing into action against them, sometimes producing shock, prostration or even death. Fortunately for us, however, these breaks in the wall are few indeed.

In addition to those parts of the nervous system through which the voluntary activities are controlled, the body has an auxiliary network of nervous tissue which provides nerves for the smooth muscle of the blood vessel walls, the digestive tract, the lungs and the heart. It also influences glandular secretions. Called the autonomic (self-governing) nervous system, this network is largely concerned with regulation of the unconscious, involuntary body functions—such as respiration and digestion—which must be carried on day or night regardless of any awareness or desire.

Before connecting with interneurons in the spinal cord, nerve cells of the autonomic system converge in a series of field stations called ganglia, which are imbedded, among other places, near or within the organs of the abdomen and thorax. The autonomic nerves and ganglia join together into small networks, or plexuses, which connect with the involuntary control centers of the brain by way of various nerve trunks.

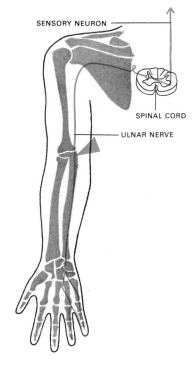

SENSORY NEURON

SPINAL CORD

ULNAR NERVE

THE ANATOMY OF A FUNNY BONE
The unsettling shock that reverberates in the fingers and courses up the spinal cord to the brain when the back of the elbow is struck is really an electric impulse, originating not in a bone but in the ulnar nerve. This nerve extends the entire length of the arm and is well protected everywhere except at that one tender spot. (The misleading term "funny bone" may have stemmed from a word play on "humerus," the large bone in the upper arm.)

Perhaps the most celebrated of these networks—particularly to aficionados of the prizefight—is the solar plexus at the pit of the stomach. Other autonomic impulses travel directly from the brain or spinal cord by nerves such as the vagus nerve, serving the stomach and upper digestive tract. Generally speaking, however, we are unaware of the existence of this auxiliary nerve network.

Virtually every animal organism has a nervous system of some sort but in the human being it has reached a higher level of development than in any other creature on earth. With a brain small enough to be operating on the amount of power that would be required to burn a 10-watt bulb, the human nervous system is thousands of times more capable than the most complex calculating machine. Man's comparatively large cerebral cortex gives him better memory, better judgment and better reasoning ability than any other creature. It permits him to make quicker and more accurate decisions. It provides him with the ability to communicate by speech, to leap intuitively to conclusions that are not clearly indicated by the information he has on hand, and to moderate his body's fight-or-flight reactions by superimposing on primitive emotions such controls as love, joy, understanding, a sense of wonder and a capability for introspection. Above all, it has given man his unique awareness of his own intelligence.

The Sense Organs: Reporters of the Outside World

The human body is, among other things, a highly tuned instrument for the perception of the external world. Vivid reports pour into man's brain through his eyes, ears, skin, nose and mouth, describing in detail the variety of things on earth. A sense of balance orients him to the earth itself. He seems to have other senses little understood at present, such as extrasensory perception. Just as it is impossible to conceive of the human head without eyes and ears, so it is impossible to conceive of a meaningful life that does not partake of the world through the senses. Experiences undergone by men in solitary confinement show that a human deprived of the external world cannot stand the effect; it is first disturbing, then terrifying—and at last the prisoner hallucinates the world he needs. To be sure, senses can mislead us, as when we see optical illusions. There are also more things on earth than our traditional five senses perceive: radio waves and gamma rays, for example. But in spite of their limitations, it is the senses that have made man the master of his environment, and the beneficiary of its wonders.

A

D

C

B

E

THE SCIENCE OF SENSING

The simple but abundant pleasures of tasting,
smelling, seeing, hearing and touching
can be described solely in terms of chemistry
and physics: wine and cheese in the mouth
(A) release chemicals which provoke the
taste buds; cells behind the nose are chemically
affected by molecules emanating from a rose
(B). The eye senses different wavelengths
reflected from Picasso's *Three Musicians* (C);
the funnel of the external ear catches air
waves set off by a violin string (D); and
the skin of the hand has thousands of nerve
endings which react to the fur of a kitten (E).
So lightning-fast is the nervous system
that in all these cases we are unaware
of bodily processes; we only enjoy.

HEARING

SEMICIRCULAR CANALS

TENSOR TYMPANI

AUDITORY NERVE

COCHLEA

EAR CANAL

EARDRUM

THREE-BONE LEVER

EUSTACHIAN TUBE

Tiny Taps on a Delicate Drum

The human ear is buffeted by stimuli from every direction—from around corners and through walls. Man hears sounds when any vibrating object pushes air molecules at a rate between 15 and 15,000 vibrations per second. The waves enter the ear canal and strike the eardrum *(left)*. The drum's vibrations travel through the middle ear, along a three-bone lever which magnifies their pressure 10 to 15 times. The bones pass them to a membrane, the oval window, behind the third bone. The window sends waves through the fluid of the snail-shaped cochlea, agitating hairs which transmit messages along the auditory nerve to the brain. There the stimulation at the end of the chain is heard as sound of a certain pitch and volume.

INNER FORTRESS

The sensitive parts of the ear are inside the skull. The fragile eardrum is protected by a muscle, the *tensor tympani,* which dampens dangerously loud noises, and by the Eustachian tube, an opening to the nose and throat which equalizes the air pressure on both sides of the drum. The semicircular canals are nonauditory organs which control balance *(pages 162-163).*

OUTER EAR   MIDDLE EAR   INNER EAR

A MECHANICAL EAR

The fanciful contraption above reconstructs the mechanical processes involved in hearing. Sound waves *(arrows)* from the bell vibrate a disklike eardrum (A) and a three-piece lever (B), which produces waves in the fluid of the cochlea (C). The small pipe (D) is the Eustachian tube. No existing machine operates in this fashion; telephones transmit sound as electrical impulses.

In a natural gesture, Mrs. Scott Carpenter shuts off the extraneous sounds entering one ear to listen to her astronaut husband's voice.

SIGHT

Light waves are readily blocked, and the eyes, unlike the ears, must be aimed at what they see. The eye operates on the same principle as the camera—the only machine directly modeled on a sense organ. The eye, however, takes two simultaneous pictures, one in black and white, the other in color. Cells in the retina, called rods, register black and white only; they are so sensitive they can detect light as feeble as a 100-trillionth of a watt. Other retinal cells, the cones, are affected by color, and are most abundant at the fovea, the place where the image falls when the eye focuses. The blind spot, lacking both rods and cones, is where the optic nerve leaves the retina, carrying its pictures for the brain to develop.

NATURAL CAMERA

Cushioned by fat, gently jiggling in its protective bony socket, the human eye is at work every waking moment, effortlessly shifting its focus from one distance to another by changing the curvature of its lens. The jellylike vitreous humor helps maintain the eye's shape, the watery aqueous humor nourishes the cornea and lens. The iris controls the admission of light.

MAN-MADE EYE

In old-fashioned cameras like the one above, a diaphragm (B) is in front of the lens (C). The diaphragm, like the iris of an eye, has an opening with a variable diameter for regulating the amount of light allowed to strike the film. An upside-down and reversed image (D) of the object (A) also appears on the retina of a human eye; it is righted in the darkroom of the mind.

Watching a flaming match, a child flexes tiny eye muscles to adjust the curvature of his lenses, causing the object to spring into focus.

TOUCH

Tidings from Close at Hand

The body's six pounds of skin, thinned out like pie dough (its average thickness is one twentieth of an inch), is a mantle of nerve endings; no other perceptions of the outer world are as intimate as the skin's tidings of warmth, softness, chill or pain. Sensations of touch are more complex than sight or hearing because most are mixtures of several stimuli. Feeling a handful of soil *(opposite)* reveals its density, texture, dampness, and the size and hardness of its particles. Each of these is reducible to two or more of the five basic skin stimuli: contact, pressure, cold, heat and pain. The dampness, for example, like wetness in general, is fundamentally a sensation of coldness.

THE TOUCHINESS OF FINGERTIPS

The human hand, designed for grasping and for touching, has up to 1,300 nerve endings per square inch. The shading in the picture above shows the varying degrees of sensitivity in the palm and three areas of the fingers. The fingertips are more sensitive than any part of the body except the lips, tongue and tip of nose, and are twice as sensitive as other parts of the hand.

A REGISTER OF SENSATIONS

The devices above symbolize the brain's reception center for touch sensations, where the component stimuli are measured for their intensity. The electric switch represents contact, the alarm bell pain, the thermometer both hot and cold, the pressure gauge weight or pressure. Combinations of these five stimuli make possible an infinite variety of touch sensations.

In the trained hand of a farmer, the feel of earth is a variety of basic touch sensations that enables him to judge the quality of the soil.

SMELL

OLFACTORY BULB

OLFACTORY MEMBRANE

MOLECULES IN A CUL-DE-SAC

In a small dead-end passage of the nasal cavity *(above)*, thousands of tiny hairs wave back and forth in the thin film of mucus that covers the olfactory membrane. When air is sniffed, it eddies into this cul-de-sac and dissolves in the mucus. The odorous molecules immediately stimulate the hairs to send signals to the olfactory bulb, which in turn relays them to the brain.

Poignant, Powerful and Fleeting

Man's sense of smell is weak compared to that of other animals, and he does not depend on it nearly so much as on sight, hearing and touch. Nevertheless, odors can seem to him both poignant and powerful. They are closely related to tastes. Most foods with marked flavors—wine, cocoa, vanilla, oranges—stimulate essentially by their aromas.

The chemistry and physics of smell are not well defined, but one recent classification considers every odor a blend of four primary smells—fragrant, acid, rancid and burnt. If the primary smells could be measured on an arbitrary scale of eight points *(below)*, every odor on earth could be labeled with a unique number based on the strength of its constituents.

=ROSE

FRAGRANT   ACID   RANCID   BURNT

MEASURING A ROSE'S AROMA

In this laboratory version of how man smells, the odorous molecules of a rose, agitated by warmth, enter the funnel and eddy down to the flask. There they are dissolved, as in the olfactory membrane and its mucus. The test tubes note the component smells that make up the aroma of a rose: strongly fragrant, moderately acid, somewhat rancid and only slightly burnt.

If the man above sniffs the roses too long, he will no longer smell them; reaction to any odor soon lessens, making way for new smells.

TASTE

HARD PALATE

PAPILLAE

PAPILLAE

LINGUAL NERVE

GLOSSOPHARYNGEAL
NERVE

An Elusive Mixture on the Tongue

Taste is the least informative of the senses. An infant is born with taste buds throughout his mouth; by adulthood most have disappeared, with those remaining mostly concentrated on the tongue. With such a depleted army of scouts, the brain often needs supporting evidence from smell, sight and touch to know what the mouth is tasting; a blindfolded person with a cold cannot distinguish between orange juice (opposite) and grapefruit juice. Taste sensations have been analyzed as blends of four primary tastes (below): sweet, sour, bitter and salty. Sweetness and saltiness are detected mostly by the buds at the tip of the tongue; the sides are most sensitive to sourness, the back to bitterness.

PUSHING FOR THE LAST DROP

The tongue (above) pushes food against the hard palate in the process of chewing. Molecules of food dissolve in saliva, and the fluid reaches the bud-shaped clusters of cells, called taste buds, in the lining of the tongue's papillae. The buds in the front and middle of tongue signal the brain via the lingual nerve; those in the rear via the glossopharyngeal nerve.

= LOLLIPOP

SWEET   SOUR   BITTER   SALT

THE UNDOING OF A LOLLIPOP

In this picture of an imaginary experiment, the molecules of a lollipop are dissolved by saliva from a medicine dropper. A chemical analysis of the sticky liquid breaks it down into the four primary tastes, just as taste buds in the mouth sort out the components of blends. This lollipop obviously tasted almost as sour as sweet, with a little bitterness and a bit of saltiness.

A girl drinking orange juice tastes acids on the sides of her tongue. She also smells citric aromas and feels the wetness and cold.

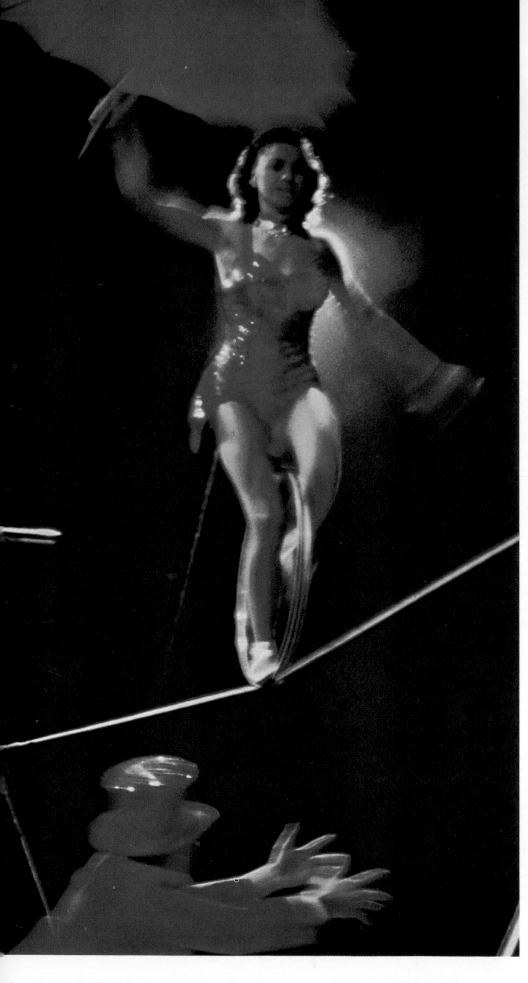

Uniting the Senses for Action

Man sees, hears and touches his environment. He also moves skillfully about in it. Virtually every one of his muscular actions, from lifting a forkful of food to the daredevil feats shown on these pages, depends on two vital senses that he seldom thinks about: the sense of balance and the muscle sense. The organs of balance are little fluid-filled structures in the inner ear. Waving in the fluid are hairs which, pulled by movements of the head and by the force of gravity, tell the brain which way the head is moving and which way is up. Thus oriented to the ground, man uses his muscle sense to evaluate messages sent from tiny nerve endings in muscles and joints which tell the brain where each movable part of the body is at any given time. Even the most ordinary actions, such as climbing up stairs, call for a smooth coordination of muscle sense with balance, sight and touch. With training and practice, the brain can learn to coordinate balance, eye and hand with such extraordinary speed that circus performers can walk high wires and juggle six flaming torches.

WALKING A WIRE
The girl in the spotlight does not fall from the tightrope into the clown's eager arms *(left)* because her mind can make extraordinarily delicate interpretations of signals from the organs of balance in her inner ear, and instantly send appropriate orders to her responsive muscles. Her muscle sense keeps her informed of the positions of her arms and legs at every moment.

JUGGLING WITH FIRE
The jugglers *(opposite)* tossing flaming torches to and fro are combining sight, touch, balance and their muscle sense with phenomenal speed. Jugglers learn to flex eye muscles and move limbs far faster than ordinary movements require, but rigorous practice can develop such quickness of eye and sureness of hand that man can play with fire without burning his fingers.

A TELLING MOUTHFUL

The French vintner about to sample one of his wines depends on the acuteness of four of his senses. He judges its color and sniffs its bouquet (odors). Then he swirls it around in his mouth, sucking in air to inhale more aromas, while tasting it for sweetness and acidity. The sense of touch within the mouth informs him of the wine's smoothness and body (density).

A Sharp Sense for Earning a Living

Some of the world's more specialized vocations indicate that man can develop his senses into a phenomenal means for measuring nuances beyond the concern of the average human being. A vintner *(left)* can taste the amounts of alcohol or acidity in a wine to within 1 per cent. Color technicians can see a difference between shades of red indistinguishable to the layman. A baker kneading dough can feel its moisture content within 2 per cent. A piano tuner *(below)* can hear the difference not only between half tones but between quarter tones. Such gifts may be partially inherited, but the evidence is that a normal human with sufficient motive can train taste, smell, hearing, sight or touch to supersensitivity. Refined sensibilities, moreover, work after business hours. The tuner's ear makes him more aware of a singer sliding off key, while the vintner is more likely than the tuner to detect the dash of cinnamon that accidentally fell in the stew.

EIGHTY-EIGHT NOTES FROM ONE
The piano tuner at right need not possess the rare gift of absolute pitch, but he must be able to hear the fine differences in vibration between notes, especially in the high and low registers where most people have difficulty. Using a single tuning fork (middle A) and a wrench, he can tune all 88 notes by comparing their vibrations to that of the fork and to each other.

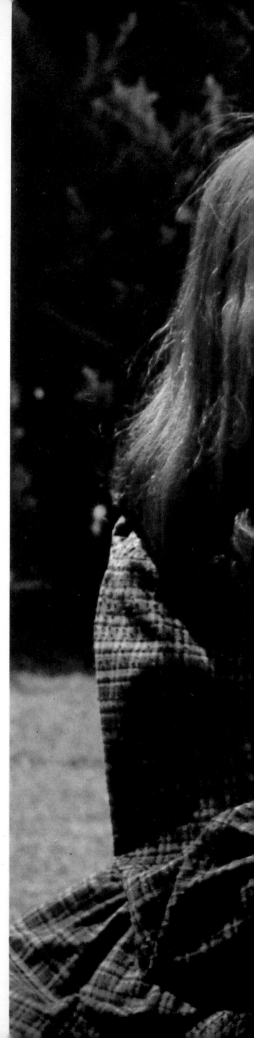

Life without Sight or Sound

More than half the human race is defective to some degree in one or more of the senses. Touch is safely distributed over the entire body, but the senses lodged in relatively localized organs, such as the eyes, are prey to accident, disease, aging and genetic malfunction. Human affairs are so involved with the senses that the result of even minor malfunctioning is bothersome: the man with the bad head cold feels cheated that he cannot enjoy his dinner. But taste and smell are probably the least vital of the senses. More serious is damage to the sense of balance from any of several diseases, including measles, which can cause a terrifying vertigo.

The most cruelly handicapped are the totally deaf or blind. Fortunately, the mind and body make amazing responses when sight or hearing is lost. The deaf learn to read lips, the blind develop acute hearing and touch.

A person deprived of both sight and hearing, like Helen Keller *(right)*, is reduced to communicating with the world through touch alone. A *cum laude* graduate of Radcliffe College and author of 12 books, Miss Keller has become a heroic example of how someone deprived of the two major senses can lead a richly rewarding life.

A TOUCH OF WOODSMANSHIP
Reaching high to grasp willow branches waving in the wind, 16-year-old Robert Mester *(above, left)*, member of a troop of blind Boy Scouts in Pennsylvania, is learning to identify different trees by the shape and texture of their leaves. He is aided by Scoutmaster Michael J. Kostie, who has been working with this troop for 20 years, teaching campcraft to blind boys.

FEELING A CONVERSATION
Unable to see or hear, the 84-year-old author Helen Keller *(opposite)* listens to a friend by feeling finger-tappings, which represent letters in the palm-manual alphabet. Her friend is Patty Duke, who played the young Helen Keller in the 1959 stage production of *The Miracle Worker,* which dramatized the formidable problems involved in training a blind and deaf child.

8

The Productive Power of Hormones

WITH ALL THE CONFIDENCE of armchair diagnosticians, many of us like to equate the state of our health with the state of certain organs of the body which, for want of specifics, we summarily label as glands. Any indisposition not otherwise identifiable is explained away by the assertion that "my glands aren't working right." Unlike other amateur dicta in the field of medicine, this one occasionally proves accurate. Certain glands do, in fact, exert enormous influence over the way we feel and the way we physically react. They wield this power through their control over that intriguing and not yet fully explored province of the body, its internal chemistry.

By definition, a gland is any cell or organ that secretes some substance. In this sense the liver, which manufactures bile, is a gland, although it plays a host of other roles as well. Basically, however, the body contains two types of gland, classified according to the way they secrete. One type is the exocrine gland, whose secretions move outward, usually by way of ducts, to some body surface, whether it be the skin itself or, for example, the lining of the digestive or respiratory tract. The second type is the endocrine gland, whose secretions move inward, without benefit of ducts, into the bloodstream.

Among the exocrines are the sweat and sebaceous glands, whose respective secretions of water and oil are evident on the skin; the mucous glands, whose mucus moistens the digestive and respiratory tract; the salivary glands, whose saliva softens food when it enters the mouth; and the mammary glands, which provide milk for the nursing infant.

The endocrines are the great chemical regulators of bodily function. It is to these glands that the layman unwittingly refers when he blames some sort of glandular mischief for his ills. The substances which are secreted by the endocrines, and which serve as their chemical messengers, are called hormones, from the Greek *hormōn,* meaning "arouse to activity." Hippocrates and his colleagues used the Greek version of the word to describe a "vital principle" which, they believed, was contained in certain body secretions and generally enlivened the body. The English version of the word is a relative newcomer to the medical lexicon. It was coined early in this century by two British physiologists, William Bayliss and Ernest Starling, who launched the fledgling science of endocrinology on its way in 1902 when they discovered and described the workings of secretin, a hormonal substance manufactured in the lining of the small intestine.

Along with the nervous system, the endocrine system serves as the major means of controlling the body's activities. The nervous system is, so to speak, built for speed; it enables the body to adjust its internal processes rapidly, as changes take place in the environment. The endocrines, on the other hand, regulate continuing processes of longer duration, in-

ON THE BRINK OF BIRTH
A full-term fetus, nearing birth, is shown in its mother's womb in this Leonardo da Vinci drawing, one of the first accurate renderings of a part of the human anatomy. The smaller sketches depict details of the uterus. Of all the many triumphs of the body, its crowning glory is the power to reproduce its kind and pass some of its vital substance on to later generations.

cluding the body's growth, sexual maturation and ability to reproduce.

Only within the past century has any real understanding of the endocrine glands been achieved. Even today we are not certain how many there are. Some are well known: the pituitary at the base of the brain; the thyroid gland in the neck; the four parathyroids lying behind the thyroid; the adrenals, perched atop the kidneys like miniature peaked caps; the insulin-making Islets of Langerhans in the pancreas; the ovaries in the abdomen of the female; the testicles in the scrotum of the male. The placenta, which feeds the unborn child, also behaves like an endocrine, manufacturing special chemicals essential to successful pregnancy. Recent studies have confirmed that the brain itself acts as an endocrine, since it, too, produces hormones.

A troop of little giants

Compared to such organs as the heart or the lungs, the endocrines seem ridiculously small and unimpressive. They are bits of tissue tucked away in obscure corners of the body; all of them together weigh no more than about five ounces. But in the widespread control they exercise over the body, they are little giants. The key to their extraordinary power lies in the hormones they secrete—among the most powerful and remarkable substances in the body.

All hormones regulate one or more chemical reactions in the body, but they seem to work in many different ways. One may alter cell membranes so that glucose from the blood can enter the cells more freely. Another may change the spatial relationship of enzymes, the chemical catalysts resident in the cells, in order to speed up metabolic reactions. Still others may stimulate production of other necessary chemicals within the cells. Precisely how any one hormone acts is still to be pinpointed: indeed, biochemists regard this problem as one of their major challenges. But this much has been established: hormonal activity must remain in delicate balance—like salt in the stew—or the entire body will be thrown out of kilter.

The endocrine gland most familiar to the layman is the thyroid, a standard topic of bridge-table talk because of its effect on weight (which is, in fact, not as great as supposed). Located at the base of the neck just below the Adam's apple, this gland can be felt from the outside, and can thus be examined by the doctor more readily than any other; an enlargement or swelling of the thyroid may be apparent even by casual observation across a room. The hormone produced by the thyroid—an iodine-protein compound called thyroxine—exercises control over the rate at which food is converted into heat and energy in all the body's cells. Without sufficient thyroxine the individual feels constantly cold, drowsy, unable to do anything without considerable exertion. His respirations are

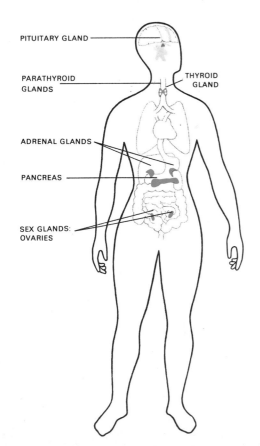

PITUITARY GLAND

PARATHYROID
GLANDS

THYROID
GLAND

ADRENAL GLANDS

PANCREAS

SEX GLANDS:
OVARIES

THE ENDOCRINE GLANDS
Endocrine glands regulate many vital body
processes. The thyroid helps control
energy production; the parathyroid distributes
calcium between blood and bone. Adrenal
glands regulate salt and water levels
and secrete stimulants; cells in the pancreas
control blood sugar. Sex glands govern
reproduction and secondary sexual
characteristics. The pituitary controls some
of the other endocrine glands.

slow, his heart rate sluggish, his appetite and sex functioning both below par; sometimes he will gain weight despite a distinctly meager diet. The opposite of this torpid syndrome of hypothyroidism is hyperthyroidism, produced by an excess of thyroxine. An individual with this condition is likely to be nervous, jittery and overactive, with a pounding heart and labored respirations, able to gorge yet lose weight, as though all the body fires were burning out of control.

Because it is relatively large and accessible, the thyroid has been known to physicians for centuries; it may have been the first endocrine gland to be discovered. Among early notions as to its function, one theory held that it lubricated and protected the vocal cords. Another suggested that it was designed to warm the throat, while esthetes insisted that it existed simply to beautify the neck. Not until 1859 were the real effects of the thyroid recognized; at that time a German anatomist, J. M. Schiff, discovered that animals whose thyroids were surgically removed developed symptoms of sluggishness and stupor. In 1891 a British physiologist, G. R. Murray, prepared an extract of sheep's thyroid that relieved similar symptoms in human patients. Two years earlier, a fellow Britisher practicing in France, Charles Brown-Séquard, had piqued the public's interest by reporting that he had successfully rejuvenated himself with extracts of animal testicular secretions. But the medical world doubted Brown-Séquard's claims, and Murray received history's accolade as the first man to cure a human endocrine disorder with a glandular extract. Today the use of such extracts to treat various malfunctions of the glands from which they originated—a procedure known as hormone replacement therapy—is common practice.

The harvest of hidden islands

In sharp contrast to the easily approachable thyroid are the best hidden of all the endocrine glands: the tiny islands of insulin-producing cells scattered throughout the pancreas. Estimates of their number range from 250,000 to 2.5 million. Another German anatomist, Paul Langerhans, first noticed them in 1869, and they are called the Islets of Langerhans in his honor. Each of these minute clumps of cells acts as a diminutive endocrine; together they make up, as it were, an organ within an organ, busily manufacturing their hormones in complete disregard for the pancreatic cells all around them, as though they were located in some completely different part of the body.

Langerhans did not, in fact, recognize what he was seeing when he observed these separate clusters of cells on his stained microscopic slides of pancreatic tissue. But nine years later a French physician, Etienne Lancereaux, detected a relationship between the pancreas and an age-old disease characterized by great hunger and thirst, wasting away of

ENDOCRINES AND GROWTH

Charles Stratton ("Tom Thumb") and his bride, Lavinia Warren, were intelligent, well-proportioned midgets less than three feet tall. Some dwarfs are victims of a thyroid malfunction, with short, misshapen limbs. An insufficiency of pituitary hormones may result in a childish but normally proportioned figure and normal intelligence. Its victims, too, are usually sterile; Tom and his bride had no children.

171

the body and ultimate death in coma. Because it was marked by the passage of excessive quantities of urine, this condition had been called "diabetes" by the ancients, after a Greek word meaning "siphon"; in 1670 Thomas Willis, physician to King Charles II of England, added "mellitus" (honey-sweet) to the name because of the quantity of sugar in the urine of diabetics. By the end of the 19th Century, medical scientists, following Lancereaux's lead, confirmed the fact that when the pancreas did not function properly, one of the body's main fuels—the simple sugar glucose—was not utilized effectively, and instead passed out of the body in urine. But they could not ascertain the substance in the pancreas which facilitated the efficient use of glucose.

Today we know that hormones manufactured in the Islets of Langerhans—insulin and the more recently discovered glucagon—between them help regulate the amount of sugar available at any time for the cells to use for the production of heat and energy. We still do not know how insulin works. One theory is that it somehow subtly changes the cell membranes so that glucose from the bloodstream can move through them into the cells more readily. When insulin is in low supply, or when its action is impeded by anti-insulin factors, diabetes mellitus develops.

In 1908 a German physician, Georg Zuelzer, prepared a crude pancreatic extract that could lower the blood-sugar levels in diabetics and make sugar disappear from their urine. This extract proved so toxic and unpredictable that its use had to be abandoned. Then, in 1921, at the University of Toronto, a Canadian surgeon, Frederick Grant Banting, teamed up with a professor of physiology, J.J.R. Macleod, and with a 22-year-old medical student at the University of Toronto, Charles Herbert Best, to try to track down the pancreatic elements responsible for the presence or absence of diabetes.

The ultimate extract

In a series of classic experiments on dogs, Banting and Best tied off the ducts leading from the pancreas. In time the pancreatic cells which produce digestive enzymes shriveled and died, but the Islets of Langerhans continued to function. By extracting the secretions of the Islets, the two men isolated the hormone insulin. Ultimately they extracted it from beef cattle in a form safe for use in the treatment of human diabetes. In 1923 Banting and Macleod were awarded the Nobel Prize for medicine for their work. Best was not so honored, perhaps because he was merely a student at the time, but today the world of medicine acknowledges that Banting and Best were equally responsible for one of the great medical breakthroughs of history. Diabetes is still incurable, but it can at least be kept under firm control.

Hormones of an equally vital if vastly different nature are produced

THE DUAL ROLE OF THE PANCREAS
The pancreas, shown below in successively increased magnifications, is located below and behind the stomach. It secretes a digestive juice by way of a duct into the small intestine, but it also contains clusters of special cells—endocrine cells within a digestive organ—called the Islets of Langerhans. Two types of cells in the clusters, alpha and beta, pour their secretions directly into the blood. Alpha cells produce a hormone called glucagon, beta cells produce insulin; both help regulate blood sugar.

PANCREAS

ISLETS
OF LANGERHANS

ALPHA
AND BETA CELLS

by the adrenal glands. Each adrenal is, in fact, two endocrine glands in one, and each secretes its own completely separate class of hormones. One type is manufactured in the central part of each adrenal, the adrenal medulla. Another type is manufactured in the outer shell of the gland, the adrenal cortex.

The hormones made in the adrenal medulla are epinephrine and norepinephrine. Both play a part in helping the body respond to emergency situations. Epinephrine, more popularly known as adrenalin from the days when it was thought to be the only hormone made by the adrenals, is a powerful stimulant with effects throughout the body. In times of stress—when we become excited, frightened or angry—epinephrine can speed up respiration, raise the blood pressure, sharpen the reflexes and put the body on guard to fight or flee. Whatever the emotion involved, we experience the same chemical reaction as a result of the epinephrine poured out into the bloodstream by the adrenals. Norepinephrine serves as an effective aide-de-camp to epinephrine at such times, causing an increase in the rate of heartbeat and constricting the skin capillaries so that blood is forced out of them and shunted, by the action of the epinephrine, to the body's major organs.

Cortisone and company

The hormones manufactured in the adrenal cortex are comparatively recent discoveries; like insulin, they were found in the course of the study of a disease, in this instance a rare one—Addison's disease. This condition, named for Thomas Addison, who first described it in 1855, is marked by muscular weakness, a peculiar bronzing of the skin, generalized apathy and collapse. Many victims of Addison's disease were found to have adrenal glands damaged by tuberculosis. Intensive research into the adrenals followed. In 1929 two biochemists, experimenting with dogs, isolated the first known hormonal compound of the adrenal cortex. By 1938 Dr. Edward Kendall of the Mayo Clinic and his co-workers had isolated no less than six different hormonal compounds which are made by the adrenal cortex, among them the now celebrated cortisone.

These hormones, unlike insulin or thyroxine, are not protein compounds, but substances which the biochemists labeled steroids, after a Greek word meaning "solid," or "firm." Because they are manufactured by the adrenal cortex they are called "adrenocortico-steroids," or "corticoids" for short. Since Kendall's pioneering, no less than 30 compounds, all of the same steroid family, have been found in the adrenal cortex.

The steroid hormones were soon shown to play a far greater role in the body than was first suspected. They help the kidneys regulate the critical balance of the salt and water content of body fluids inside and outside the cells. They also influence the body's ability to build up and break down proteins, to form antibodies against bacteria and viruses, to repair damaged tissue, and to control inflammation. Indeed, because of their ability to suppress inflammation of joints and to reduce scarring of inflamed joint capsules, these hormones work almost miraculously to relieve pain and retard permanent damage in rheumatoid arthritis. Corticoids also reduce inflammation in nephrosis and rheumatic fever, speed the healing of skin wounds, and help in the treatment of gout.

A bonanza in beef cattle

Originally the steroids could be obtained only with great difficulty; one early researcher had to grind up a ton of the adrenal glands of beef cattle in order to secure less than a half ounce of one particular hormonal compound. But since that time a succession of steroids has been synthesized in the laboratory.

While in most cases the hormones manufactured by one endocrine gland differ considerably from those made by other endocrine glands, the adrenal cortical hormones are structurally very similar to those secreted by the sex glands—the female ovaries and the male testes. These hormones—testosterone and androsterone in the male, estrogen and progesterone in the female—are actually produced in both sexes. But the male sex hormones normally predominate in men, the female sex hormones in women.

During childhood, production of sex hormones is very low. As the male approaches sexual maturity, however, the testes begin secreting more and more of the male hormones. These substances effect striking growth changes such as the development of beard and muscles, the enlargement of the larynx (with a resulting deepening of the voice), the maturation of sex organs and the development of sexual urges. They are also believed to stimulate sperm production in the testicles. In the female, the female sex hormones bring about the development of the hips and breasts, and other so-called secondary sex characteristics that mark the female of the species. In addition, they act to prepare the uterus to receive and sustain a fertilized ovum. If conception does not occur when an ovum has been freed from the ovary, soft blood tissue is cast off from the uterus; within a period of weeks, it is again prepared to receive and sustain the next ovum that is released, should it be fertilized by a sperm. In short, the cycle of menstruation experienced by all nubile females is a direct result of the waxing and waning of hormones on a more or less monthly schedule.

Despite the fact that hormones have widely different functions, and are produced in different parts of the body, they do not go their merry way independent of any regulation. Some higher form of control is required to determine, for example, when more thyroid hormone is needed and when production should slow down, when adrenal cortical hormones are needed and when not. The gland which fulfills this master role is the pituitary, one of the tiniest endocrines of all. It controls the hormonal output not only of the thyroid gland and adrenal cortex, but also of the sex glands.

The pituitary hangs from the bottom of the brain by a little stalk just above the nasal passage. Vesalius, who named it, mistakenly believed that it discharged mucus into the nose, and therefore he derived the name from the Latin word for "nasal secretion." The pituitary is insignificant in appearance—about the size of an acorn—but it packs an extremely powerful punch. Like the adrenals, the pituitary is actually two glands in one—posterior and anterior. Of the two, the posterior pituitary manufactures no hormones of its own, but stores two that are initially secreted in a part of the brain known as the hypothalamus. These hormones are oxytocin, which is believed to stimulate labor at the end of pregnancy, and vasopressin, which helps the body retain its fluids. The anterior part of the pituitary, however, is what gives this potent endocrine gland its major claim to sovereignty. One hormone secreted in the anterior pituitary controls the over-all growth of the body. Five more have the task of spurring hormone production in other endocrine glands.

The quirks of growth

The growth hormone, sometimes called somatotropin, regulates the growth of bone, muscle and other tissues from top to toe. In some individuals, fortunately only a few, underproduction or overproduction of somatotropin occurs during childhood. Either extreme causes growth abnormalities. Underproduction results in dwarfism; the pituitary dwarf almost never attains adult proportions or sexual maturity, although his I.Q. is normal. Overproduction results in gigantism; one of the most famous victims of this condition was Robert Wadlow of Alton, Illinois, who died in 1940. Wadlow towered 8 feet 11 inches high, weighed 495 pounds and had feet almost 20 inches long.

Most of us, happily, need have little concern with somatotropin, since its aberrations are the exception. Of considerably greater urgency for the average person are the anterior pituitary hormones which regulate other endocrines. One of these, the thyroid-stimulating hormone, TSH, signals the thyroid to manufacture thyroxine when the level gets too low. The adrenocorticotrophic hormone, ACTH, stimulates production of the steroid hormones by the adrenal cortex. Three other anterior pituitary hormones are vital to sex functioning. The follicle-stimulating hormone, FSH, stimulates the testes to produce sperm and the ovaries to secrete

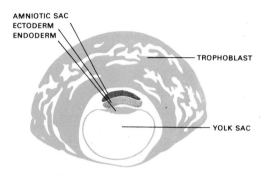

A 12-DAY-OLD EMBRYO
Every hour of the human gestation period proceeds on a rigid schedule. By the 12th day, the embryo has become two vitally different cell layers, the endoderm, forming the roof of a vestigial yolk sac, and the ectoderm, at the base of the undeveloped amniotic sac. The trophoblast is a surrounding mass of cells which nourish the embryo.

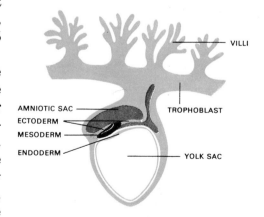

PROGRESS ON THE 15TH DAY
Cell differentiation continues, and the mesoderm develops from the ectoderm. The ectoderm will form outer tissues and the nervous system; the mesoderm blood vessels, muscle, bone and many organs; the endoderm interior linings. The trophoblast and its villi, which absorb nourishment from the uterine wall, will become the placenta.

estrogen. The luteinizing hormone, LH, spurs hormone production in the sex glands of both men and women. Production of the female sex hormone progesterone, in particular, is abetted by the lactogenic hormone, LTH, which also stimulates the mammary glands to produce milk.

Endocrine control works both ways. Just as a thermostat, which fires a furnace into activity when the room temperature drops, is itself turned off when the temperature rises high enough, the production of each of the stimulating hormones in the pituitary is suppressed by the presence in the blood of the hormone which it stimulated. Thus, as the level of thyroxine drops, TSH is poured out to goad the thyroid cells into activity; but as soon as production has been speeded up, the very presence of thyroid hormone in quantity in the bloodstream blocks the pituitary's release of more TSH until thyroid activity slows down again. The result of this cycle is the maintenance of a remarkably steady balance of thyroid hormone in the bloodstream at all times. Such a feedback system serves to regulate levels of adrenal hormones and sex hormones in much the same way.

A view from the frontier

For all we have learned about the endocrine glands during the past century, there is reason to suspect that we are still only on the frontiers of understanding them. Virtually every week something new is discovered—or researchers discover that what they thought was a simple fact about an endocrine or hormone is actually a good deal more complicated. Much recent work, for instance, has focused on control of the production of the stimulating hormones in the anterior pituitary. Evidence has irrefutably established that a direct connection exists between the endocrines, the brain and the entire nervous system. Endocrinologists investigating the neurohormones—the links between the nervous system and the endocrine system—have concluded that both systems are actually different sectors of one vast body-controlling organ system, each influencing the other and each dependent upon the functioning of the other for the maintenance of the body's total well-being. The interactions between the two are many and varied; without sufficient thyroid hormone, for example, the nervous system will fail to mature properly.

But all the unfolding intricacies of the body's chemical regulators and nervous system, and indeed all the discoveries which man has made about the structure and function of his body, would seem pointless indeed were it not for the fact that the death of an individual does not necessarily end his or her contribution to the human species. Like most other living organisms, the human body has one capability that gives it a certain claim to physical immortality: the ability to reproduce itself, to pass part of its body substance directly along to future generations.

THE GROWTH OF AN EMBRYO

During the first 12 weeks of pregnancy, the embryo develops from a single cell into a recognizable human being. In the uterus, the embryo is cushioned against shock by the soft uterine wall and wrapped in the fluid-filled amniotic sac. In the first illustration, the embryo is about a fifth of an inch long. The vestigial yolk sac, almost useless in the gestation of man, is relatively large. By the fifth week, buds for arms and legs are advanced, the mouth is forming and eyes appear. Sex organs form as ridges on the kidneys. By the sixth week, fingers are forming and the mouth begins to draw into shape; the embryo's tail has been all but absorbed. By the 12th week, the small being is called a fetus, and has such human characteristics as a well-established nose, lips, cheeks, eyelids and ears.

4-WEEK EMBRYO   5-WEEK EMBRYO   6-WEEK EMBRYO

AMNIOTIC SAC   EMBRYO   PLACENTA   AMNIOTIC SAC   AMNIOTIC SAC

YOLK SAC

UTERUS

UTERINE CAVITY

YOLK SAC

Certain of the cells of the body—the male sperm and the female ovum, or egg—are the seeds from which new and unique individual members of the species can grow.

For the first 24 hours after the egg is fertilized by the sperm it seems simply to rest, as if gathering strength for the difficult job ahead. Then it begins to divide rapidly into new cells. For several days the new cells appear precisely the same as the old, forming a round blob of tissue shaped like a hollow ball—the embryo. But then a few of the cells begin to vary from the others. The embryo dents in upon itself to form a tiny cuplike structure; the cup stretches out to become an elongated pouch. The cells lining the inside of the pouch begin to look taller and thinner than those on the outside. By the 12th day after conception, two distinct layers of cells—the inner and the outer—have formed. Next, a third layer of cells begins to appear between these two. By the middle of the third week the original ovum has produced three quite separate layers of so-called precursor cells—the ectoderm or outer layer; the endoderm, or inner layer; and the mesoderm, or middle layer. Soon these begin to form the organs of a rudimentary human body.

By transplanting cells from one point to another on the embryos of chicks, experimenters have tried to pinpoint the moment when—and the reason why—the early cells from the fertilized ovum begin to vary and form precursor tissue. All they have learned to date is that up to a point the transplanted chick cells seem to melt back into the undifferentiated embryo, while beyond this point they proceed to form into the same precursor cells they would have formed into had they not been transplanted.

Soon after they appear, the precursor cells, too, differentiate. The endoderm elongates to become a primitive gut, which then forms pockets, or buds, that develop into tiny airtubes, lungs, liver and digestive organs. The ectoderm forms a crease along the back of the embryo which later differentiates into the nervous tissue of the spinal cord and brain; other parts of the ectoderm form the skin, hair, nails and sensory organs. From the mesoderm, bone and muscle and connective tissue begin to emerge; so do the kidneys and the blood vessels.

Auguries of a masterwork

By the end of three months the fetus—while still no more than three inches in length—has developed virtually every detail of its basic structure. The remaining six months are devoted almost solely to the growth and refinement of this new body. Fingerprints appear; lung tissue is perfected for later use in breathing; muscles grow and are exercised (which accounts for the lusty kicking which the pregnant woman frequently feels). When the baby is finally born we see a completely finished, loudly squalling human being with each of its many parts working

12-WEEK FETUS

AMNIOTIC SAC

UMBILICAL CORD

perfectly—all arisen from a single living cell which has proliferated almost beyond belief.

The marvelous mechanism for reproducing the species assures us that these bodies of ours, with their complex structure and function, serve a continuing purpose. But it also presents us with an inescapable fact: it is nature, not man, that has devised this most amazing, delicate, powerful organism ever to appear on earth. Everything we have learned about the body has been learned with nature's sufferance. The most brilliant and imaginative researcher knows—or soon learns—that nature must be with him and not against him if his work is ultimately to succeed.

Above all, those who study the human body feel more and more wonder at this remarkable organism and its capabilities the more they learn about it. No man-made devices are ever likely to rival it either in complexity or efficiency. Recently Dr. Charles Bradford, a distinguished Boston orthopedist, summed up the feelings that must regularly inspire those entrusted with the body's care: "The doctor observes the anatomical perfection of the hand, and the stabilizing microphones of the ear, and the television screens of the retina, and the multiple batteries of electronic computers in the brain, and from all these he gains a new reverence for the incomprehensible power that created man, so anxiously and so wonderfully wrought."

The Making of a Doctor

From the priestly medicine men of ancient Egypt to the dexterous surgeons of a modern operating room, those who have ministered to the sicknesses of the human body have been generally accorded mankind's grateful respect. Selflessly, physicians labor to destroy the reasons for their professional existence. In ancient and in modern times, medicine has exacted from its students a longer, more costly apprenticeship than any other calling. Today it requires at least eight years of higher education, at a cost of more than $15,000, before a graduate can make his initial bid for patients (opposite). The process by which a student is metamorphosed into an M.D. is arduous and often tedious; some of the more important steps are shown in this photographic essay by Alfred Eisenstaedt. Many of these scenes reflect the deep satisfactions of a physician's life—a diagnosis perceptively reached, a life-or-death operation successfully performed.

A SIGN PROUDLY HUNG
Dr. Joseph Colson, 34 and a father of five, announces his office is open in Beverly, Massachusetts. After college he taught agricultural chemistry for three years to save enough money for his medical training. Having studied and worked so hard for this moment, Dr. Colson let his sign reflect his determined struggle: he made it himself from a mahogany packing case.

Recruiting Future M.D.s

AN AUDIENCE THROUGH THE DAY
Frederick Nurnberg *(above, center)*, who has wanted to be a doctor for "so long I don't remember," watches Dr. John Maerz examine a patient in his Oaks, Pennsylvania, office. Fred, a 17-year-old high-school senior, spent 14 hours observing how an M.D. works and lives.

A FUTURE THROUGH THE WINDOW
A baby is born by Cesarean section at Beth Israel Hospital, Newark, New Jersey, as the Future Physicians Club of a nearby high school watches from behind glass *(right)*. Visits like this help prepare club members to understand what it means—and takes—to be a physician.

180

"Into whatever houses I may enter, I will go for the benefit of the sick," reads the physician's 2,000-year-old Hippocratic oath. The oath's ancient words lay bare an even more ancient truth: medicine is more than merely another way to make a living; it is membership in a fraternity with an austere code of ethics.

In its current campaign to instill the ethical code and the fraternal sense in the doctors of the future, the medical profession is guiding interested high school students through the intricacies of medicine. Project MORE (Medicine's Organized Recruitment Endeavor) arranges for teenagers to visit local doctors, sharing their home life and their hours with patients (*opposite*). High schools with Future Physicians Clubs dispatch their members to watch major operations (*below*), to tour hospital wards and even to practice minor medical procedures such as taking a patient's blood pressure. More than 50 per cent of club members are girls—incisive testimony that acceptance of women doctors has come a long way since 1847, when Elizabeth Blackwell, the first female to graduate from an American medical school, was denounced as being either insane or a "bad woman."

AT A MATHEMATICS LECTURE
A lecture in finite mathematics engrosses Donald Hight, 21 *(above),* a Dartmouth premedical student. Most candidates for medical school take twice as much mathematics as biology.

STUDYING AN EMBRYO
Peering through a microscope at the cross section of a salamander's embryo *(above)* is Stanford Roman, 21, a premedical student at Dartmouth College. A psychology major, he hopes to become a pediatrician. He considered a career in law or teaching, but decided on medicine because it "demands a lot of the individual . . . dealing with other people's lives."

IN THE LABORATORY
Helping a coed perform a delicate titration of acids and alkalis *(right)* in the freshman chemistry laboratory at Oberlin College is Ronald Saunders, 22, a senior laboratory assistant doing honors work in organic chemistry. He gave thought to the ministry, but decided on a career in medicine because it offers a chance "to combine science and working with people."

Pre-Medicine's Long Preparation

Although most medical schools will accept students who have completed only three years of college, the tense, feverish competition for admission prompts most candidates to take the full four years before beginning their professional training. For the doctor-to-be, college means long afternoons in laboratories and evenings in libraries. Most medical schools require him to have taken many courses in the sciences: 20 semester hours of chemistry, eight hours of biology or zoology, eight hours of physics, 16 hours of mathematics. But medicine is more than science. The physician must be able to express himself to his patients, to treat the whole person, not merely the illness. Realizing this, medical schools also require an undergraduate to take at least 12 semester hours of English, 24 hours of the social sciences and humanities, and to acquire a reading knowledge of French, German or Spanish. With such a work load, a premedical student usually studies harder than most. But for him the toil seems a small price for the coveted reward achieved by only half of those who seek it: a letter from a medical school that says, "You have been accepted."

Dissecting Death to Study Life

In his first year of medical school, the student studies anatomy (the geography of the body), physiology (how the different organs do their various jobs) and biochemistry (the chemical reactions that make life work). The indelible experience of the student's first year is the time he spends hunched over a cadaver in the anatomy laboratory. There, with a partner (*above*), he painstakingly dissects a human cadaver until he knows its anatomy from the bone structures of the head to the skin layers of the sole.

The four main courses of the second year are pathology (what disease does to the body), bacteriology (how microorganisms cause disease), pharmacology (when and how drugs are used to treat disease) and physical diagnosis (identification of disease).

IN THE ANATOMY LAB
Two freshmen medical students *(above)* at the University of Illinois College of Medicine slice through the abdominal wall of the human cadaver whose lessons they will share. Queasy at first, the students soon come to consider the anatomy laboratory an invaluable experience.

Learning
from the Living

Steeped in the knowledge gained from books and laboratory work, the student in the second half of medical school is at last allowed to treat (under supervision) real patients. In the hospital wards, he is taught how to examine patients *(right)* and is allowed to do physicals on his own *(opposite, below)*. Sometimes he may even be asked to diagnose a difficult case *(below)*. Throughout his fourth year, often treating the same patients on their repeated visits to the hospital's clinic, he may learn the meaning of that unteachable intangible, the doctor-patient relationship. And although there is still classroom work, less emphasis is placed on formal lectures. But the year's final emphasis is formal indeed: the cap-and-gown commencement ceremony where the student is presented with the diploma inscribed *Doctoris in Arte Medica*— "for a doctor in the art of medicine."

A THUMPING GOOD LESSON
Making the rounds of a ward, interns and medical students *(above)* watch a staff doctor thump a patient's back. Such "percussing" produces sounds which the students learn to detect as dull (usually meaning disease in the chest) or resonant (usually indicating a healthy chest).

A WHITE-FROCKED INQUISITION
Pointing to X-rays as he presents his diagnosis of an actual hospital patient, the medical student at left will soon be interrogated by his audience. The inquisitors: M.D.s, who will criticize his diagnosis; and fellow students, who will be encouraged to ask trenchant questions.

WORKING UP TO MEDICINE

The third-year medical student at left is examining a patient's throat as part of his "work up" —a medical term for giving a new hospital patient a physical exam and writing up his medical history. To catch students' mistakes, staff doctors give such patients a second work up.

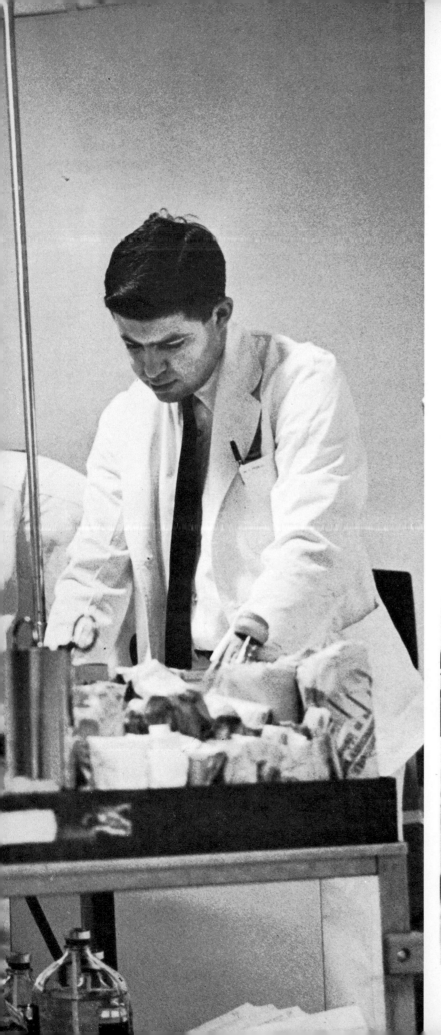

An Intern's Grueling Initiation

An M.D. diploma is not a license to practice medicine. In most states, the new graduate is required to work at least one more year as an intern, or subordinate member of a hospital's staff, before he can be certified a full-fledged physician.

An intern must work up new patients, may assist in surgery and obstetrics, serve on ambulance duty and spend long nights in the emergency room *(left)*, where he absorbs a growing maturity in medicine along with his strong coffee. His average weekly salary is small—about $58. His average condition is a state of exhaustion.

But exhausted as they usually are, interns like Dr. Stuart Perkal *(left and below)* betray a glow of satisfaction. The tedium of textbooks is over; their medical careers have begun.

NO TIME FOR TEXTBOOKS
Intern Stuart Perkal *(left,* at table) checks heartbeats on the electrocardiograph while a nurse and staff doctor labor to save the life of a cerebral hemorrhage victim in Baltimore's Sinai Hospital. Emergency-room service usually allows Dr. Perkal only brief snatches of sleep *(below).*

189

The Last Apprenticeship

When his internship is over, the licensed M.D. is qualified to open his office as a general practitioner. But if he chooses to join the 50 per cent of practicing physicians who are specialists, his training has just begun. He must now join a hospital as a resident M.D. to learn from and to assist senior staff doctors who practice the specialty of his choice.

The length of a residency varies, depending on the specialty, from two to six years. The average starting salary is $70 a week. A resident's hours may be shorter than an intern's, but his responsibilities are heavier. While learning from experienced specialists above him, the resident is in turn expected to dispense his knowledge to the interns and students below him (*right*). In this way, he has begun to assume the traditional triple role of the mature physician: practitioner, teacher and lifetime student of medicine.

SURGEON-INSTRUCTOR
Quietly lecturing to an intern and a student as he performs a gall bladder-common duct operation is Dr. Charles McKhann Jr. (*right,* wearing glasses), a resident in surgery at Boston's Massachusetts General Hospital. Dr. McKhann presides over an average of 10 operations a week.

190

The Many Ways to Gauge the Body

Few objects have been as thoroughly scrutinized by modern science as the human body. It has been measured and weighed in all manner of ways; its capacities and functions have been calculated and evaluated in minute detail. Of the mountains of data which have been gradually accumulated, some of the items of most direct interest to the layman are reported on this and on the following two pages.

On page 194 is a map showing the life expectancy of men and women by countries and a table of the energy output of both sexes according to activity. And on page 195 is a chart of salient structural and physiological differences between the sexes. The table below lists the normal range and the known maximums and minimums of certain bodily measures and functions, along with some statistics on childbearing.

THE WIDE RANGE OF HUMAN STATISTICS

MEASURE	NORMAL	MAXIMUM	MINIMUM
HEIGHT	Men: 4'3"-6'7" Women: 3'11"-6'1½"	The tallest man on record was Robert Wadlow of Illinois, who stood 8'11". He was a victim of pituitary gigantism.	The shortest person on record was a 16-inch dwarf reported by Georges Buffon, a French naturalist, in the late 18th Century.
WEIGHT	Men: 112-204 lbs. Women: 92-173 lbs. (U.S.)	Robert Hughes of Illinois weighed 1,069 lbs. shortly before his death in 1958.	Hopkin Hopkins, a Welsh boy who died at the age of 17, never weighed more than 17 lbs.
NUMBER OF HAIRS ON HEAD	120,000 (average)	Natural blondes can have as many as 140,000.	The minimum (excluding baldness) usually occurs among natural redheads, who can have as few as 90,000.
BODY TEMPERATURE	97-99°F.	At 110° F., fatal hemorrhages occur, and cells degenerate and die. Recovery from temperatures higher than 110° is extremely rare.	At 79.5°F., the heart fails. One rare exception was a girl who recovered from a low of 60.8°F.
HEART BEATS PER MINUTE	70	In young people, during strenuous exercise, the heart may beat as often as 270 times a minute.	55-60 (during sleep).
BLOOD PRESSURE	120/80 mm. (at age 20)	A person with severe hypertension may develop pressure as high as 300/150—i.e., 300 mm. of pressure when the heart is contracted, 150 when relaxed.	Just after birth, pressure may be as low as 74/38.
SLEEP NEEDED PER DAY	7-9 hrs. (adults)	Newborn babies require 18 to 20 hrs. a day.	Oldsters may get along on as little as 5 hrs. a day.
SIZE OF BABIES AT BIRTH	7.3 lbs. (median)	The largest baby on record was a 23¾-lb. son born to a 7½-foot Nova Scotian giantess, Mrs. Anna Bates, in 1879. Mr. Bates was 7'8" tall, weighed 470 pounds.	The smallest baby known to have survived was a 12-oz. girl born in the U.S. in 1936.
BIRTHS PER MOTHER	2.4 (U.S.)	A Russian peasant woman gave birth to 69 children—16 sets of twins, 7 sets of triplets and 4 sets of quadruplets. Few survived infancy.	
CHILDBEARING AGE	25.4 (median, 1961)	In 1863 a child was born to a 69-year-old Cincinnati woman.	In 1939 a child was born to a 5-year-old Peruvian Indian girl.

LIFE EXPECTANCIES AROUND THE WORLD

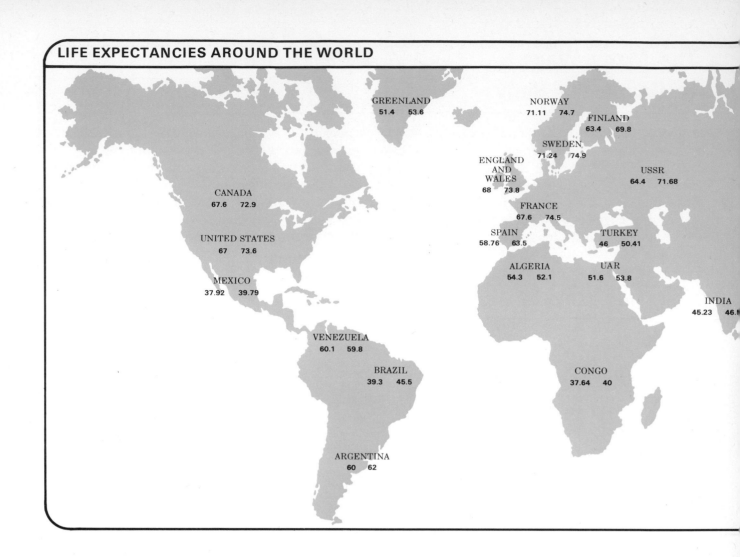

GREENLAND
51.4 53.6

NORWAY
71.11 74.7

FINLAND
63.4 69.8

SWEDEN
71.24 74.9

ENGLAND
AND
WALES
68 73.8

USSR
64.4 71.68

CANADA
67.6 72.9

FRANCE
67.6 74.5

UNITED STATES
67 73.6

SPAIN
58.76 63.5

TURKEY
46 50.41

MEXICO
37.92 39.79

ALGERIA
54.3 52.1

UAR
51.6 53.8

INDIA
45.23 46.

VENEZUELA
60.1 59.8

BRAZIL
39.3 45.5

CONGO
37.64 40

ARGENTINA
60 62

THE ENERGY SPENT BY WOMEN AND MEN

WOMEN	CALORIES	MEN	CALORIES
LYING AT REST	.98	LYING AT REST	1.19
STANDING	1.11	STANDING	1.25
OFFICE WORK	1.31-1.72	OFFICE WORK	1.6
PEELING POTATOES	1.29	PEELING POTATOES	2.7
WASHING DISHES	1.53	WASHING DISHES	3.3
WASHING AND DRESSING	3.3	WASHING AND DRESSING	3.56
WALKING	2.9	WALKING	5.1
MAKING BEDS	5.4	MAKING BEDS	7
SKIING ON LEVEL HARD SNOW	10.8	SKIING ON LEVEL HARD SNOW	9.9

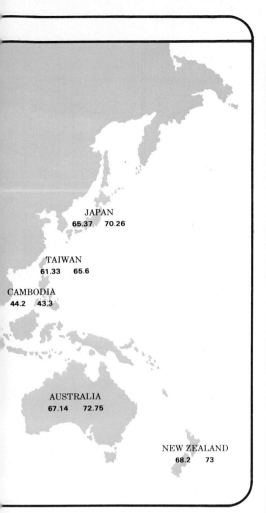

JAPAN
65.37   70.26

TAIWAN
61.33   65.6

CAMBODIA
44.2   43.3

AUSTRALIA
67.14   72.75

NEW ZEALAND
68.2   73

THE SPAN OF LIFE. Improved nutrition, medical care and hygienic practices have combined to lengthen life appreciably almost everywhere in the world (*map above*). In each country life-expectancy figures for males are shown at left, for females at right.

THE MEASURE OF ENERGY. The body uses two thirds of the energy it gets from food for vital processes. This energy is gauged in calories, the heat-producing value of food. Some common pursuits and the energy they consume per minute are listed at left.

THE SCOPE OF VARIATION. Beyond observable distinctions between men and women, there are innumerable contrasts in both the composition of the body and the way it performs. Some of these, between healthy adults of the two sexes, are listed at right.

SOME DIFFERENCES BETWEEN THE SEXES

MEASURE	WOMEN	MEN
WEIGHT OF BRAIN		
Small	37.04 ozs.	38.8 ozs.
Average	44.98 ozs.	49.38 ozs.
Large	54.68 ozs.	60 ozs.
WEIGHT OF HEART	8 ozs.	10 ozs.
QUANTITY OF BLOOD	.875 gal.	1.5 gals.
SURFACE AREA OF SKIN	1.93 sq. yds.	2.21 sq. yds.
WATER: % OF BODY WEIGHT	54%	60%
MUSCLE: % OF BODY WEIGHT	36%	42%
FAT: % OF BODY WEIGHT	28%	18%
BONE: % OF BODY WEIGHT	10%	10%
AVERAGE LENGTH OF SPINE	24 ins.	28 ins.
TOTAL LUNG CAPACITY AT AGE 25		
Small	3.28 qts.	4.54 qts.
Average	4.44 qts.	6.76 qts.
Large	5.7 qts.	9.51 qts.
NUMBER OF BREATHS PER MINUTE (AT REST)	20-22	14-18
INTAKE OF AIR PER BREATH		
Resting	.358 qt.	.793 qt.
Light work	.909 qt.	1.77 qts.
Heavy work	.93 qt.	2.15 qts.
Deepest possible intake (vital capacity) at age 25	3.17 qts.	5.18 qts.
NUMBER OF RED BLOOD CELLS PER CUBIC MILLIMETER (BLOOD COUNT)—U.S. AVERAGE	4,200,000-5,400,000	4,600,000-6,200,000

BIBLIOGRAPHY

General

Asimov, Isaac, *The Human Body*. Houghton Mifflin Company, 1963.

Best, Charles B. and Norman Burke Taylor, *The Living Body*. Holt, Rinehart & Winston, 1958.

Carlson, Anton J., Victor Johnson and H. Mead Cavert, *The Machinery of the Body*. The University of Chicago Press, 1961.

Clendening, Dr. Logan, *The Human Body*. Alfred A. Knopf, 1959.

King, Barry G. and Mary Jane Showers, *Human Anatomy and Physiology*. W. B. Saunders, 1963.

Miller, Benjamin F. and Ruth Goode, *Man and His Body*. Simon & Schuster, 1960.

*Sproul, Edith E., *The Science Book of the Human Body*. Franklin Watts, Inc., 1955.

†Tokay, Elbert, *The Human Body and How it Works*. Signet Books, New American Library, 1957.

History

†Atkinson, Donald T., *Magic, Myth and Medicine*. Premier Book, Fawcett World Library, 1958.

Castiglioni, Arturo, *History of Medicine*. Alfred A. Knopf, 1947.

Major, Ralph, *History of Medicine*. Vol. I, II. C. C. Thomas, 1954.

†Singer, Charles, *A Short History of Anatomy and Physiology from the Greeks to Harvey*. Dover Publications Inc., 1957.

Biography

†Calder, Ritchie, *Medicine and Man*. New American Library, 1958.

Sarton, George A., *Galen of Pergamon*. University of Kansas, 1954.

†Shippen, Katherine B., *Men of Medicine*. Viking Press, 1959.

†Sigerist, Henry E., *The Great Doctors*. Anchor Books, Doubleday, 1958.

Special Subjects

Asimov, Isaac, *The Human Brain*. Houghton Mifflin, 1963.

†Beaumont, William S., *Observations on the Gastric Juice and Physiology of Digestion*. Dover, 1959.

*Buddenbrock, Wolfgang von, *The Senses*. University of Michigan Press, 1958.

†Galambos, Robert, *Nerves and Muscles*. Anchor Books, Doubleday, 1962.

†Giusti, George and Rudolf Hoffmann, *Heart: Anatomy, Function and Diseases*. Dell, 1962.

Milne, Lorus J. and Margery, *The Senses of Animals and Man*. Atheneum, 1962.

Nourse, Alan E., *So You Want to Be a Doctor*. Harper & Row, 1963.

Ranson, Stephen Walter, and Samuel L. Clark, *The Anatomy of the Nervous System*. W. B. Saunders, 1963.

*Von Neumann, John, *The Computer and the Brain*. Yale University Press, 1958.

Walker, Kenneth, *The Story of Blood*. Herbert Jenkins Ltd., London, 1958.

Woodburne, Russell T., *Essentials of Human Anatomy*. Oxford University Press, 1961.

*Wooldridge, Dean H., *The Machinery of the Brain*. McGraw-Hill, 1963.

*Also available in paperback.

†Only in paperback.

ACKNOWLEDGMENTS

The editors of this book are especially indebted to Dr. Lawrence E. Hinkle Jr., Clinical Associate Professor of Medicine and Clinical Associate Professor of Medicine in Psychiatry at the New York Hospital-Cornell Medical Center, who served as general consultant, and to the following persons and institutions who helped in the preparation of the book: Norman Budde, American Medical Association; Dr. Farrington Daniels, Associate Professor of Medicine, New York Hospital-Cornell Medical Center; Dr. Gustave J. Dammin, Pathologist-in-Chief, Peter Bent Brigham Hospital, Boston; Dartmouth College; William DeLay, Director of Public Relations, American Academy of General Practice, Kansas City, Missouri; Dr. Ivan Dunaief, Kings County Hospital, Brooklyn; Dr. Douglas C. Eaglesham, Director, Department of Radiology, Guelph General Hospital, Ontario, Canada; Dr. Ralph L. Engle Jr., Associate Professor of Medicine, New York Hospital-Cornell Medical Center; Essex County Medical Society, East Orange, New Jersey; Dr. Henry Fischer, Assistant Curator, Egyptian Collection, Metropolitan Museum of Art; Dr. Donald H. Ford, Associate Professor of Anatomy, State University of New York, Downstate Medical Center, Brooklyn; Dr. Wilbur D. Hagamen Jr., Associate Professor of Anatomy, New York Hospital-Cornell Medical Center; Dr. Sami Hashim, Director, Laboratory of Metabolic and Nutritional Research, Saint Luke's Hospital, New York City; Dr. James G. Hirsch, Associate Professor of Medicine and Microbiology, The Rockefeller Institute, New York City; Dr. Allan E. Inglis, Hospital for Special Surgery, New York City; Roy Keaton, Director, Magazine Relations, American Medical Association; Frederick Kilgour, Librarian, Yale Medical Library, Yale University; Dr. Hymen S. Mayerson, Chairman, Department of Physiology, Tulane University School of Medicine; Dr. Richard Manegold, American Medical Association; The Massachusetts General Hospital; Dr. Edmund McNally, Chief of Gastroenterology, Kings County Hospital, Brooklyn; Dr. Ade T. Milhorat, Director, Institute for Muscle Disease, New York City; Dr. Charles R. Noback, Professor of Anatomy, College of Physicians and Surgeons, Columbia University; Oberlin College; Dr. Carl Pfaffman, Department of Psychology, Brown University; Duncan M. Potter Jr., General Manager, Special Instruments Laboratory, Inc., Knoxville; Presbyterian-Saint Luke's Hospital, Chicago; E. F. Richner, Manager, News Services, Public Relations Dept., Eastman Kodak Company, Rochester, New York; Dr. Alfred A. Rosenthal, New York City; Dr. Albert L. Rubin, Associate Professor of Medicine, New York Hospital-Cornell Medical Center; Dr. Alexander Sandow, Chief, Division of Physiology, Institute for Muscle Disease, New York City; Sinai Hospital of Baltimore; Loren B. Sjöström, Vice-President, Arthur D. Little, Inc., Cambridge, Massachusetts; Leon Summit, Editor, *Spectrum*, Charles Pfizer and Co., Inc., New York City; Dr. Roy Swan, Professor (Chairman) of Anatomy, New York Hospital-Cornell Medical Center; Beverley Tarlov, New York Hospital-Cornell Medical Center; Dr. David D. Thompson, Associate Professor of Medicine, New York Hospital-Cornell Medical Center; Dorothy S. Ullmann, New York Hospital-Cornell Medical Center; University of Illinois College of Medicine, Chicago; Alice D. Weaver, and Librarians of the Rare Book Department, The New York Academy of Medicine; Alfred F. Zobel, Director of Public Relations, Hoffmann-La Roche, Inc., Nutley, New Jersey.

INDEX

Numerals in italics indicate a photograph or painting of the subject mentioned.

PICTURE CREDITS

The sources for the illustrations which appear in this book are shown below. Credits for pictures from left to right are separated by commas, from top to bottom by dashes.

Cover—Lee Boltin

CHAPTER 1: 8—Bob Landry. 10, 11—Drawings by Nicholas Fasciano. 12—Bottom, Derek Bayes. 13—The Bettmann Archive. 15—Derek Bayes. 17—Eric Schaal courtesy Yale University Medical Library. 18, 19—H. Lund Hans courtesy Danish National Museum, Hamburg Museum Für Völkerkunde—J. R. Eyerman courtesy Museum of Man, San Diego. 20—Courtesy Roemer-Pelizaeus Museum, Hildesheim, Germany. 21—Khamis Abdel Latif courtesy Cairo Museum, Henry Groskinsky courtesy the Metropolitan Museum of Art, Rogers Fund, 1929. 22—Emmett Bright courtesy Naples National Museum. 23—Aldo Durazzi courtesy Piacenza City Museum—Derek Bayes courtesy British Museum. 24—Bodleian Library, Oxford. 25—Bodleian Library, Oxford, except top: Khamis Abdel Latif courtesy Museum of Islamic Arts, Cairo. 26, 27—Giraudon courtesy Condé Art Museum, Chantilly, France. 28—Courtesy British Museum, Vatican Library. 29—The Pierpont Morgan Library. 30, 31—Courtesy British Museum. 32, 33—Color by Fritz Kredel of Vesalius drawings courtesy University of Padua Library.

CHAPTER 2: 34—Robert W. Kelley. 36, 37—Drawings by Nicholas Fasciano. 38—Drawings by George Schwenk. 40—Drawings by George Schwenk. 41—Drawing by Charles Gottlieb. 43—Drawings by Elliot Herman and Paul Calle. 44, 45—Drawings by Elliot Herman and Paul Davis. 46 through 53—Drawings by Elliot Herman and Paul Calle.

CHAPTER 3: 54—Bob Gomel for SPORTS ILLUSTRATED. 56—Drawing by Adolph E. Brotman and Charles Mikolaycak. 57—The Bettmann Archive. 58, 59, 60—Drawings by Richard Boland. 62—Drawing by Mark A. Binn. 63—Drawing by Joe Lambandero adapted from illustration by Professor D. Denny-Brown in *Reflex Activity of the Spinal Cord,* Oxford University Press. 65—Andreas Feininger. 66—Courtesy Bethlehem Steel Co. 67—Gjon Mili. 68, 69—Top, Andreas Feininger; bottom, G. Gheradi-A. Fiorelli. 70, 71—Andreas Feininger, Carl Iwasaki. 72—Gjon Mili. 74—Oscar Savio. 75—Gjon Mili.

CHAPTER 4: 76—George Silk. 78—Eric Schaal courtesy Academy of Medicine. 79—Drawing by Adolph E. Brotman. 80, 81—Drawings by Otto van Eersel. 82—Drawings by Nicholas Fasciano adapted from illustration by Bunji Tagawa in *Scientific American.* 84—The Bettmann Archive. 85—Courtesy Simone Gossner.

87, 88—Fritz Goro. 89—Top, Don Wong from Photo Researchers, Inc. 90, 91—PIP-ZFA. 92—Dr. G. Douglas Talbott—Dr. James Hirsch. 93—Dr. James Hirsch. 94, 95—Andreas Feininger except left, Fritz Goro. 96—Dan Bernstein. 97—Fritz Goro.

CHAPTER 5: 98—Alfred Eisenstaedt. 100—Drawing by Joe Lambandero. 101—Drawing by Nicholas Fasciano. 103—Drawing by Nicholas Fasciano. 104, 105—Drawings by Otto van Eersel. 106—Eric Schaal courtesy Yale University. 109 through 117—Drawings by Push Pin Studio.

CHAPTER 6: 118—Monte Casazza. 121—Drawing by Otto van Eersel. 122—Drawings by Charles Mikolaycak. 124, 125—Drawings by George V. Kelvin. 127—Lee Johnson. 128—Travenol Laboratories, Inc.—drawing by Dan Todd. 129—J. R. Eyerman—Mark Kauffman. 130, 131—Eliot Elisofon. 132—Top, Don Hinkle; bottom, courtesy Dr. Gustave J. Dammin, Peter Bent Brigham Hospital, Boston. 133—Drawings by Max A. Gschwind for FORTUNE. 134—Drawing by R. M. Chapin Jr. for TIME. 135—Dr. John Retan. 136—Ted Polumbaum. 137—Al Fenn. 138—Gordon Tenney. 139—Fritz Goro.

CHAPTER 7: 140—Sam Nocella. 142—Drawings by George Schwenk. 144—Drawing by Adolph E. Brotman. 145—Drawing by George V. Kelvin. 147—Drawings by Otto van Eersel. 148, 149—Drawings by Nicholas Fasciano. 151—Norman Snyder. 152—Drawing by Jack J. Kunz—drawing by Lowell Hess. 153—Ralph Morse. 154—Drawing by Jack J. Kunz—drawing by Lowell Hess. 155—Wayne Miller from Magnum. 156—Drawing by Jack J. Kunz—drawing by Lowell Hess. 157—Edward Clark. 158—Drawing by Caroll Jones—drawing by Lowell Hess. 159—A. Y. Owen. 160—Drawing by Caroll Jones—drawing by Lowell Hess. 161—Carroll Seghers II. 162—Ronny Jaques from Photo Researchers, Inc. 163—George Karger from PIX. 164, 165—Brian Seed from Black Star, Lee Johnson. 166, 167—John Launois from Black Star, Nina Leen.

CHAPTER 8: 168—Dr. Heinz Zinram. 170—Drawing by Nicholas Fasciano. 171—Museum of the City of New York. 172—Drawings by George V. Kelvin. 175, 176, 177—Drawings by Adolph E. Brotman. 179 through 191—Alfred Eisenstaedt. 194—Map by Nicholas Fasciano.

PRODUCTION STAFF FOR TIME INCORPORATED

Arthur R. Murphy Jr. (Vice President and Director of Production), Robert E. Foy, James P. Menton and Caroline Ferri
Text photocomposed under the direction of Albert J. Dunn and Arthur J. Dunn

Printed by R. R. Donnelley & Sons Company, Crawfordsville, Indiana,
and Livermore and Knight Co., a division of Printing Corporation of America, Providence, Rhode Island
Bound by R. R. Donnelley & Sons Company, Crawfordsville, Indiana
Paper by The Mead Corporation, Dayton, Ohio
Cover stock by The Plastic Coating Corporation, Holyoke, Massachusetts